This book belongs to:

. . . .

Words alive
Words aloud
Spoken alone
Or in a crowd
Words to learn
Words to remember
From January
Until December

Words Aloud!

BOOK 1

Poetry, Prose and Drama
to Read, Learn and Share

Chosen by Anne Harvey

We would like to thank:

Dr Diana Devlin and Susan Ford for the valuable contribution they have made to the development of this publication.

Editorial Director: **Eric Hollis**

Managing Editor: **Godfrey Salter**

Department of Initial Studies, Guildhall School of Music & Drama
Barbican, London EC2Y 8DT. Tel: 0171 382 7167

WORDS ALOUD!

This book has many different uses. It offers a wide variety of poems, prose and drama to read at home or school, to learn by heart for performance and above all to enjoy.

You might choose a theme from a book, add ideas of your own and make a written or spoken anthology. You might choose a writer or two contrasting writers and discover more about them. You might join with friends for a class, or school assembly or concert, or entertain your friends and family at home. You might prepare pieces for an examination or festival competition.

Sometimes only an extract from a longer story or play is printed. You will need to read the whole work to know what it is all about. To help you find the original books, look at the information on pages 81-84.

Anne Harvey

Contents

Contents

Some One

Some one came knocking
  At my wee, small door;
Some one came knocking,
  I'm sure — sure — sure;
I listened, I opened,
  I looked to left and right,
But nought there was a-stirring
  In the still dark night;
Only the busy beetle
  Tap-tapping in the wall,
Only from the forest
  The screech-owl's call,
Only the cricket whistling
  While the dewdrops fall,
So I know not who came knocking,
  At all, at all, at all.

WALTER DE LA MARE

One Stormy Night

One stormy night the wind was howling, the iron gate
creaked, and the black cat hissed. Inside the house the
fire-light flickered, and, roused from his sleep, the
old dog barked.
The great oak door of the barn flew open.
The grey mare neighed and a white owl screeched.
Then, just before dawn, the wind fell silent, a bright
star shone and the sky was clear.
For some a new day was beginning.
But others slept on, in the morning sun.

RUTH BROWN

from Alfie's Feet

Alfie's boots were very smart and shiny but they felt funny.

Alfie wanted to go out again right away. So he put on his
mac, and Dad took his book and his newspaper and they
went off to the park.

Alfie stamped in a lot of mud and walked through a lot of
puddles, splish, splash, SPLOSH! He frightened some
sparrows who were having a bath. He even frightened two
big ducks. They went hurrying back to their pond, walking
with their feet turned in.

Alfie looked down at his feet. They still felt funny. They
kept turning outwards. Dad was sitting on a bench. They
both looked at Alfie's feet.

Suddenly Alfie knew what was wrong!

SHIRLEY HUGHES

New Shoes

My shoes are new and squeaky shoes,
They're very shiny, creaky shoes,
I wish I had my leaky shoes
That Mummy threw away.

I liked my old brown leaky shoes
Much better than these creaky shoes,
These shiny, creaky, squeaky shoes
I've got to wear today.

ANONYMOUS

Mrs Button

When Mrs Button, of a morning,
Comes creaking down the street,
You hear her old two black boots whisper
'Poor feet — poor feet — poor feet!'

When Mrs Button, every Monday,
Sweeps the chapel neat,
All down the long, hushed aisles they whisper
'Poor feet — poor feet — poor feet!'

Mrs Button after dinner
(It is her Sunday treat)
Sits down and takes her two black boots off
And rests her two poor feet.

JAMES REEVES

3

Give Yourself A Hug

Give yourself a hug
when you feel unloved

Give yourself a hug
when people put on airs
to make you feel a bug

Give yourself a hug
when everyone seems to give you
a cold-shoulder shrug

Give yourself a hug —
a big big hug

And keep on singing,
'Only one in a million like me
Only one in a million-billion-thrillion-zillion
like me.'

GRACE NICHOLS

Florence Talltrees

Oh my name is Florence Talltrees
but they call me Honey Flo.
I'm a singer and a dancer
and I play the old banjo.
        Sing and shout now —
        dancing as we go.
Oh my name is Florence Talltrees
but they call me Honey Flo.

Oh I come from Tooting Broadway
with a banjo on my knee,
and I'm off to Chipping Campden
my dear, true love for to see.
        Sing and shout now —
        dance along with me.
Oh I come from Tooting Broadway
with a banjo on my knee.

NANCY CHAMBERS

The Sycamore Tree

I think I can
Said Mary Ann:
I'm sure you can't
Said Mary's aunt:
It all depends
Said Mary's friends.
So Mary's mother
And sister and brother
Discussed the matter
With one another.
They whispered together
Arguing whether
They should agree
To let her climb
The Sycamore Tree.
They thought that they oughtn't
To give their permission
For the tree was in such a
Neglected condition.
But while they were talking
Without a stop
Mary Ann
Had climbed to the top.
And there she balanced
(Without permission)
At the tippermost top
In a topply position!

JONATHAN ALWAYS

King Rollo and the Tree

King Rollo was in the garden
'I'm going to climb that tree,' he said.
'Don't climb the tree, you'll get your hands dirty,' said the magician.
'I'm still going to climb that tree,' said King Rollo.
'Don't climb the tree, you will tear your jacket,' said Cook.
'I'm going to climb very high,' said King Rollo.
'Don't climb the tree, you'll fall and hurt yourself,' said Queen Gwen.
'I'm going to climb right to the top,' said King Rollo.
Hamlet the cat said nothing.
King Rollo started to climb.
'Mmm,' said the magician.
King Rollo climbed and climbed.
'Tut, tut,' said Cook.
King Rollo climbed very high.
'Oh dear,' said Queen Gwen.
King Rollo climbed right to the very top.
Then King Rollo slipped.
All the way down the tree he slipped and slid and slid and slipped.
Finally he landed on the ground with a BUMP!
'I said you would get your hands dirty,' said the magician.
'I said you would tear your jacket,' said Cook.
'I said you would fall and hurt yourself,' said Queen Gwen.
'And I said I would climb to the top,' said King Rollo.
'Yes,' said Queen Gwen, 'and you did.'

DAVID McKEE

Swing Song

Here I go up in my swing
    Ever so high.
I am the King of the fields, and the King
    Of the town.
I am the King of the earth, and the King
    Of the sky.
Here I go up in my swing ...
    Now I go down.

A. A. MILNE

Bridesmaid

On the hanger on my bedroom door
is a dress like a princess's.

If I was seven or eight or nine
or ten I'd be too big,
it wouldn't fit. But I'm six,

and six is just right
to wear a dress like a princess's
with a satin sash
that creaks like crisp snow
and white satin ballet shoes.

But I'm six
and six is just right
to wear a comb of silk flowers
in my hair,
a dress like a princess's,
a satin sash
that creaks like crisp snow,
white satin ballet shoes,
and walk up the long aisle of the church
carrying a basket of spring flowers.

Six is exactly right.

MICK GOWAR

7

Three Little Girls

Three little girls were sitting on a rail,
   Sitting on a rail,
   Sitting on a rail;
Three little girls were sitting on a rail,
  On a fine hot day in September.

What did they talk about that fine day,
   That fine day,
   That fine day?
What did they talk about that fine day,
  That fine hot day in September?

The crows and the corn they talked about,
   Talked about,
   Talked about;
But nobody knows what was said by the crows,
  On that fine hot day in September.

KATE GREENAWAY

Caterpillar, Caterpillar

My father and my grandfather both liked gardening very
much, but my grandfather used to grow stinging nettles.
My father didn't; he said they were weeds, and rooted
them out.
'Why don't you get rid of your nettles?' I asked my
grandfather.
'Stinging nettles grow butterflies,' he said. 'Go and look.'
I went and looked. I couldn't see any butterflies, though.
My grandfather turned one of the nettle leaves over to
show me the bumps on the back of it, but I didn't know
what they were.

'Butterfly eggs,' said my grandfather.
'What sort of butterflies ?'
My grandfather peered closely at the bumps. 'Haven't got
my specs on,' he said, 'but they could be Tortoiseshells, or
Peacocks. They both like nettles. If you keep an eye on
them you'll see when the caterpillars hatch out.'
'Won't they crawl away ?' I asked.
My grandfather straightened up and looked down at me.
'Humph,' he said. 'You just keep watching.'
So I did.

VIVIAN FRENCH

Caterpillar

Brown and furry
Caterpillar in a hurry,
Take your walk
To the shady leaf, or stalk,
Or what not,
Which may be the chosen spot.
No toad spy you,
Hovering bird of prey pass by you;
Spin and die,
To live again a butterfly.

**CHRISTINA
ROSSETTI**

9

The Barn Owl

High up on the rafters
Something white
Sleeps in the shadows
Waiting for the night.

High up from the rafters
Something flies,
With silent wings
And big round eyes.

RICHARD JAMES

The Tawny Owl

Autumn night, a great shiny moon —
Owls cry and cry over the sleeping farms:
'To-whoo! To-whoo! To-whoo!
Poor Jenny Hoolet's feet are a-cold!'

A mouse
Sneaks out to a corn-stack, begins
To nibble the spilt grain. Suddenly,
On noiseless downy wings, with never a whisper, Death
Swoops down from the frosty air.

JOHN HEATH-STUBBS

Owl Babies

Once there were three baby owls:
Sarah and Percy and Bill.
They lived in a hole
in the trunk of a tree
with their Owl Mother.
The hole had twigs and
leaves and owl feathers in it.
It was their house.
One night they woke up and
their Owl Mother was GONE.
'Where's Mummy?' asked Sarah.
'Oh my goodness!' said Percy.
'I want my Mummy!' said Bill.
The baby owls thought
(all owls think a lot) —
'I think she's gone hunting,' said Sarah.
'To get us our food!' said Percy.
'I want my Mummy!' said Bill.
But their Owl Mother didn't come.
The baby owls came out of
their house and they sat
on the tree and waited.

MARTIN WADDELL

That's What We'd Do

If you were an owl,
    And I were an owl,
And this were a tree,
    And the moon came out,
    I know what we'd do.
We would stand, we two,
On a bough of the tree;
You'd wink at me,
And I'd wink at you;
That's what we'd do,
    Beyond a doubt.

I'd give you a rose
For your lovely nose,
And you'd look at me
    Without turning about.
I know what we'd do
(That is, I and you);
Why, you'd sing to me,
And I'd sing to you;
That's what we'd do,
    When the moon came out.

MARY MAPES DODGE

19

from The King of the Blue Lagoon

One day Sally went to the seaside again. She took the stone with her. Sally waded into the sea, holding the stone in her cupped hands. She squatted, and the sea washed over the stone and rocked it against her fingers.

The sea was a grey, cold sea. Sally thought it would change, but it didn't. Nothing changed. The sea was grey; the rocks were grey; the sky was grey. But suddenly, in Sally's hands, the stone came alive. It twitched. It wiggled. It slithered and slipped. Sally looked down and saw that the stone had changed to a fish: a bright, bright fish with a rose-red body and turquoise stripes, golden eyes with black rims, fins that flicked silver and a rose-red shimmering tail. On its head was a crown.

'Oh!' said Sally. She was so surprised that she opened her fingers and the fish slipped through.

Before she could catch it, it flicked its tail and wiggled its body and swam away, bright as a jewel in the grey sea. Sally watched it grow smaller, and smaller, until at last it was no bigger than a sequin. Then it disappeared.

ANN TURNBULL

Fishes' Evening Song

Flip flop,
Flip flap,
Slip slap,
Lip lap;
Water sounds,
Soothing sounds.
We fan our fins
As we lie
Resting here
Eye to eye.
Water falls
Drop by drop,
Plip plop,
Drip drop,
Plink plunk,
Splash splish;
Fish fins fan,
Fish tails swish,
Swush, swash,
swish.

This we wish ...
Water cold,
Water clear,
Water smooth,
Just to soothe
Sleepy fish.

DAHLOV IPCAR

Regent's Park

What makes the ducks in the pond, I wonder,
Go suddenly under?

Down they go in the neatest way;
You'd be surprised at the time they stay.
You stand on the bank and you wait and stare
Trying to think what they do down there;
And, just as you're feeling anxious, then
Suddenly up they come again
Ever so far from where you guessed,
Dry and tidy and self-possessed.

What is it makes the ducks, I wonder,
Go suddenly under?

ROSE FYLEMAN

Ducks' Ditty

All along the backwater,
Through the rushes tall,
Ducks are a-dabbling,
Up tails all!

Ducks' tails, drakes' tails,
Yellow feet a-quiver,
Yellow bills all out of sight
Busy in the river!

Slushy green undergrowth
Where the roach swim —
Here we keep our larder,
Cool and full and dim.

Every one for what he likes!
We like to be
Heads down, tails up,
Dabbling free!

High in the blue above
Swifts whirl and call —
We are down a-dabbling
Up tails all!

KENNETH GRAHAME

The Wind

I can get through a doorway without any key,
And strip the leaves from the great oak tree.

I can drive storm-clouds and shake tall towers,
Or steal through a garden and not wake the flowers.

Seas I can move and ships I can sink;
I can carry a house-top or the scent of a pink.

When I am angry I can rave and riot;
And when I am spent, I lie quiet as quiet.

JAMES REEVES

The Wind

Who has seen the wind?
  Neither I nor you:
But when the leaves hang trembling
  The wind is passing thro'.

Who has seen the wind?
  Neither you nor I:
But when the trees bow down their heads
  The wind is passing by.

CHRISTINA ROSSETTI

Rain

I opened my eyes
And looked up at the rain
And it dripped in my head
And flowed into my brain
So pardon this wild crazy thing I just said
I'm just not the same since there's rain in my head.
I step very softly
I walk very slow
I can't do a hand-stand
Or I might overflow.
And all I can hear as I lie in my bed
Is the slishity-slosh of the rain in my head.

SHEL SILVERSTEIN

from Three Raindrops

A raindrop was falling out of a cloud, and it said to the
raindrop next to it: 'I'm the biggest and best raindrop in the
whole sky!'
'You are indeed a fine raindrop,' said the second, 'but you
are not nearly so beautifully shaped as I am. And in my
opinion it's shape that counts, and *I* am therefore the best
raindrop in the whole sky.'
The first raindrop replied: 'Let us settle this matter once
and for all.' So they asked a third raindrop to decide
between them.
But the third raindrop said: 'What nonsense you're both
talking! *You* may be a big raindrop, and *you* are certainly
well-shaped, but, as everybody knows, it's purity that really
counts, and I am purer than either of you. *I* am therefore
the best raindrop in the whole sky!'
Well, before either of the other raindrops could reply,
they all three hit the ground and became part of a
very muddy puddle.

TERRY JONES

Puddle

The Muddy Puddle

The rain had left a puddle on the path. A shining smooth puddle like a mirror. Sally could see her face in it. She sploshed her finger into the place where her mouth laughed back at her. That made her puddle face hide behind little rings of glinting water. They grew wider and wider to melt into the puddle's edge.

Sally took out her finger. She waited for the water to become still again. To become a glassy smooth puddle like a mirror to see her face in once more.

JEAN CHAPMAN

I am sitting
In the middle
Of a rather Muddy
Puddle,
With my bottom
Full of bubbles
And my rubbers
Full of Mud.

While my jacket
And my sweater
Go on slowly
Getting wetter
As I very
Slowly settle
To the Bottom
Of the Mud.

And I find that
What a person
With a puddle
Round his middle
Thinks of mostly
In the muddle
Is the muddi-
Ness of Mud.

DENNIS LEE

The Dog in the Manger

Once upon a time there was a farm-dog who found his way into the stable, jumped into the manger, and made himself very snug in a bed of soft hay. When the horses came in after a long day's work in the fields, they were horribly hungry. They made straight for their manger, sniffing the delicious hay. But the dog was comfortable and did not like being disturbed.

'Would you move ?' asked the horses politely. 'You're lying on our dinner, and we're so hungry we could eat a haystack.'

'Too bad,' answered the dog. 'I'm very comfortable, and I'm so tired I could sleep for a week.'

So the selfish dog lay on the hay — though of course *he* couldn't eat it. The horses stayed horribly hungry, and wished he would find somewhere else for a bed.

AESOP

Keeping Christmas

How will you your Christmas keep?
Feasting, fasting, or asleep?
Will you laugh or will you pray,
Or will you forget the day?

Be it kept with joy or prayer,
Keep of either some to spare;
Whatsoever brings the day,
Do not keep but give away.

ELEANOR FARJEON

from Father Christmas and The Donkey

The donkey waited and listened. He could hear footsteps crunching a little on the frosty grass. Then he saw somebody coming towards him — somebody tall and big in a long, shaggy, white fur coat with a white fur hood pulled up over his head and big, fur-topped boots on his feet. As he came nearer, the donkey could see that he had a long, white beard, and under his white fur hood his eyes shone and twinkled like two bright stars. There was a large sack upon his shoulders. It was tied in the middle, but both ends bulged and hung down as if it was full of interesting things of all shapes and sizes. He was puffing a little, as if the sack was heavy to carry up the hill. His breath was like a little cloud in the frosty air. He looked at the donkey and the donkey looked at him.

The donkey was feeling still more excited. He was happy too, not grumpy any more. There seemed to be a wonderful, kind, warm, friendly feeling all around. And then a very kind voice said, 'Happy Christmas, friend donkey. I heard you calling and you sounded lonely, so I came.'

'I was lonely,' said the donkey, 'and I'm glad you came. Excuse my asking, but would you mind telling me who you are?'

ELIZABETH CLARK

The Donkey

Her home is built of wind and sun,
Bird's song and butterfly's wings;
Roof of sky,
Carpet of grass —
And the seasons hang their pictures on the wall.

Her eyes are wise and mild and kind,
Her muzzle as soft as pussy-willow,
And her enormous ears hear things that we will never know
For sometimes
She thinks she remembers a dream,
Like sounds of singing, a stable, a child —
And one great, glorious star.

ANNE BELL

from A Little House of Your Own

When the grownups were eating supper I lived under the dining-room table and nobody could see me. Nobody knew where I was.
I lived under the dining room table and looked at my picture book and under the dining room table was just like a house for me. A secret house. Nobody could see me. Nobody could find me ...
And all the time I was in my secret house, my under the table house, my little house all to myself.
There are many kinds of secret houses. There are many places where you can have your own little house.
This is what I mean ...
When I grew too big to live under the dining room table I had another secret house up in a tree.
Nobody could see me in my secret house in the tree. When people looked up in the tree they couldn't see me at all.
All they could see were the many many leaves. But I could look down and see everyone if I wanted to.

I could see my mother digging in the garden.
I could see my father lying in the hammock.
I could see the dog scratching fleas.
I could see the cat chasing a butterfly.
I could see everybody if I wanted to.
But nobody could see me in my secret house up in the tree.

BEATRICE SCHENK DE REGNIERS

Tea Party

The teapot's full, the cups are clean,
the cloth is white, the grass is green,
the jam is sweet, the cakes are good,
the sunlight smiles as sunlight should;
but only crickets sing with me,
and only shadows drink my tea.

I know a word that no one knows;
I know a place where no one goes.
If sometime, in the smiling sun
(when all the cricket songs are done,
and shadows all have drunk their tea)
a friend should come to visit me,
I'll show the place where darkness bites,
and speak the word the silence writes.

RUSSELL HOBAN

Keziah

I have a secret place to go.
Not anyone may know.
And sometimes when the wind is rough
I cannot get there fast enough.

And sometimes when my mother
Is scolding my big brother,
My special place, it seems to me,
Is quite the only place to be.

GWENDOLYN BROOKS

from The Wonderful Cake-Horse

A man once made a cake shaped like a horse. That night a shooting star flew over the house and a spark happened to fall on the cake-horse. Well, the cake-horse lay there for a few moments. Then it gave a snort. Then it whinnied, scrambled to its legs, and shook its mane of white icing, and stood there in the moonlight, gazing round at the world.

The man, who was asleep in bed, heard the noise and looked out of the window, and saw his cake-horse running around the garden, bucking and snorting, just as if it had been a real wild horse.

'Hey! cake-horse!' cried the man. 'What are you doing?'

'Aren't I a fine horse!' cried the cake-horse. 'You can ride me if you like.'

But the man said: 'You've got no horse-shoes and you've got no saddle, and you're only made of cake!'

The cake-horse snorted and bucked and kicked the air, and galloped across the garden, and leapt clean over the gate, and disappeared into the night.

TERRY JONES

The Speller's Bag

Here a bone.
Here a stone.
In my bag
I keep them all.

A stone brought me
by the sea.
A bone taken from where
I'll never tell thee.

A bone, a stone,
a feather, a shell,
all in my bag
to cast a spell.

A shell that taught
the wind to howl.
A feather stolen
from the back of an owl.

Then again it might be
from a raven's neck.
I'll never tell thee.

Look inside all who dare.

Inside my bag
you'll find your fear.

JOHN AGARD

The Wasp

When the ripe pears droop heavily,
The yellow wasp hums loud and long
His hot and drowsy summer song.
A yellow flame he seems to be,
When darting suddenly from high
He lights where fallen peaches lie.

Yellow and black — this tiny thing's
A tiger soul on elfin wings.

WILLIAM SHARP

An Injured Wasp

He cannot fly, but his wings are reaching for the sky
and trying to pull his too-heavy body up into the
blue world above.
His shivering wings make a sound like my dad's shaver.
I wonder where he comes from, and how did he hurt
his wing? I let him crawl on my finger, and hope
he will not sting me.
All six legs chase after one another.
The tips of his legs feel gentle and itchy as he
struggles across my hand. I have to scratch my palm.
His lovely body is sunflower-striped, and his head is
streamlined, with big staring eyes that don't move.
In my hand he seems quite content, not struggling, so
I feel his head delicately with the tip of my first finger.
The tiny hairs feel like soft cotton, and the wings are
like cracked glass. If I place him carefully on a yellow
flower his hurt wing might heal.

DAVID JOHN BARRETT

The Fly

How large unto the tiny fly
Must little things appear! —
A rosebud like a featherbed,
Its prickle like a spear;

A dew-drop like a looking glass,
A hair like golden wire;
The smallest grain of mustard-seed
As fierce as coals of fire;

A loaf of bread, a lofty hill;
A wasp, a cruel leopard;
And specks of salt as bright to see
As lambkins to a shepherd.

WALTER DE LA MARE

The Intruder

Two-boots in the forest walks,
Pushing through the bracken stalks.
Vanishing like a puff of smoke,
Nimbletail flies up the oak.

Longears helter-skelter shoots
Into his house among the roots.
At work upon the highest bark.
Tapperbill knocks off to hark.

Painted-wings through sun and shade
Flounces off along the glade.
Not a creature lingers by,
When clumping Two-boots comes to pry.

JAMES REEVES

25

from Pete and the Ladybird

She was an orange-coloured ladybird with three big spots. 'Hello, ladybird,' Peter said, as she went past his shoe. But she didn't answer.

Pete very carefully kneeled down on the pavement, and put his finger in front of the ladybird. She thought about his finger. Pete could see her thinking. Then just as he thought she didn't like his finger, she decided that she did. She climbed on to it, and Pete slowly stood up.

Then he walked along carefully. He was taking the ladybird home.

He was looking so hard at the ladybird as he walked along carefully, that he bumped right into a window cleaner. The window-cleaner was propping up a ladder against the wall.

'Look out!' he shouted. 'Where d'you think you're going?'

But Pete was staring at his finger. The ladybird had gone. She had opened her wings and flown straight into the wind. And now he couldn't see her anywhere.

He turned to the window-cleaner. He was very upset.

'You've lost my ladybird,' he said tearfully. 'I was taking her home and she was going to live in my matchbox, and now she's gone and she'll get lost, and it's all your fault ...'

'Hush,' said the man, flapping his duster in front of Pete's face.

Pete was rather surprised at that, and he hushed.

LEILA BERG

Little Trotty Wagtail

Little Trotty Wagtail, he went in the rain,
And tittering tottering sideways, he ne'er got straight again,
He stooped to get a worm, and look'd up to catch a fly,
And then he flew away ere his feathers they were dry.

Little Trotty Wagtail, he waddled in the mud,
And left his little footmarks, trample where he would.
He waddled in the water-pudge, and waggle went his tail,
And chirrupt up his wings to dry upon the garden rail.

Little Trotty Wagtail, you nimble all about,
And in the dimpling water-pudge you waddle in and out,
Your home is nigh at hand, and in the warm pigsty,
So, little Master Wagtail, I'll bid you a good-bye.

JOHN CLARE

from The Short Voyage of Albert Ross

Steven sat up. He was not dead. The leeches sank back into the weeds and the water snakes slunk away to their lair. The river curled quietly past the sand bank and the steel band played peaceful tunes in the rushes.

John didn't seem very pleased to see him. 'Look what you've done! Look what you've done! You idiot! You *nitwit!*' he shouted, jumping up and down in the sand. 'You've sunk the raft.'

'It was my raft.'

'You've lost it.'

'I've lost my boots.'

John took Steven by the collar, and by the hair, and shook him until he stood up.

'Go and get it.'

'What ?'

'Go and get the raft.'

Steven was used to getting things for John. 'If you don't do what I say,' John would whisper, 'I'll tell your mum what you did,' or, 'I'll tell your mum what you said to the dustman,' and Steven always did as he was told.

Now he looked at the water, and the green satin weed where the snakes and the leeches and the mud lay waiting.

'No,' he said.

JAN MARK

27

The Glass Slipper

CINDERELLA:

> I wish plates didn't get greasy,
> I wish stockings didn't get holes,
> And sweeping and scouring and scrubbing were easy,
> I wish
> There weren't coals.
>
> I wish bells didn't keep ringing,
> And tablecloths never got tears,
> Or stoves wanted blacking or beans wanted stringing
> I wish
> There weren't stairs.
>
> I wish meals didn't want laying,
> I wish they ate out of a dish,
> I wish there was more time for laughing and playing,
> I wish ...
> I wish ...
>
> I wish I could be like the others,
> I wish there was no one to scold,
> I wish that I wasn't afraid of stepmothers,
> And didn't
> Feel cold.

This won't do, Ella. It won't, just because you can't go to the ball! Put on your shawl, silly, and be sensible. Lots of people all over the world can't go to balls. If you've got to get sticks, you've got to get sticks. *(opens door)* And the woods look lovely in the snow. I wish ... I wish ... And the snow looks lovely in the woods. I wish ... How lovely it would be if everything was lovely! I wish ... I wish ...
(She moves out into the snow.)

ELEANOR AND HERBERT FARJEON

Cinderella's Song

Oh, little cat beside my stool,
My tabby cat, my ashy one,
I'll tell you something in your ear,
It's I can put the slipper on.

The cinders all will brush away,
Oh, little cat beside my chair,
And I am very beautiful
When I comb down my hair.

My dress was gold, my dress was blue,
But you could hardly think of that.
My dress came to me through the air,
Oh, little cinder cat.

My dress is gone a little while,
My dress was sweet and blue and cool,
But it will come again to me,
Oh, little cat beside my stool.

ELIZABETH MADOX ROBERTS

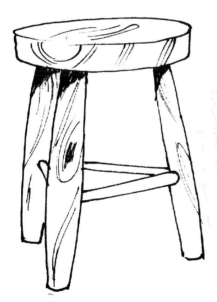

The Gingerbread Man

The gingerbread man gave a gingery shout:
'Quick! Open the oven and let me out!'
He stood up straight in his baking pan.
He jumped to the floor and away he ran.
'Catch me,' he called, 'if you can, can, can.'

The gingerbread man met a cock and a pig
And a dog that was brown and twice as big
As himself. But he called to them all as he ran,
'You can't catch a runaway gingerbread man.'

The gingerbread man met a reaper and sower.
The gingerbread man met a thresher and mower;
But no matter how fast they scampered and ran,
They couldn't catch up with the gingerbread man.

Then he came to a fox and he turned to face him.
He dared Old Reynard to follow and chase him;
But when he stepped under the fox's nose
Something happened. What do you suppose ?
The fox gave a snap. The fox gave a yawn,
And the gingerbread man was gone, gone, GONE.

ROWENA BENNETT

from The Gingerbread Boy

Once upon a time there lived a little old woman and a little old man. One day, when the little old woman was baking, she made a little boy out of gingerbread. She gave him two black currants for eyes, and a piece of green marzipan for a nose, and a big red cherry for a mouth. Then she popped him in the oven to bake.

Presently, she heard a tiny voice in the oven saying, 'Let me out, let me out.' The little old woman ran and opened the oven door, and what do you think — out hopped the little gingerbread boy!

'Goodness gracious me!' cried the little old woman, and before she knew what was happening, the little gingerbread

boy had hopped out through the door and into the street.
The little old woman and the little old man ran after him.
'Stop, stop, Gingerbread Boy!' they called. But he only
looked back and cried,

      'Run, run, as fast as you can.
      You can't catch me,
      I'm the gingerbread man.'

And they could not catch him.

   Soon he met a cow. 'Stop, stop, Gingerbread Boy!' called
the cow. But he only looked back and cried,

      'Run, run, as fast as you can.
      You can't catch me,
      I'm the gingerbread man.'

And the cow could not catch him.

   Soon he met a horse. 'Stop, stop, Gingerbread Boy!'
called the horse. But he only looked back and cried,

      'Run, run, as fast as you can.
      You can't catch me,
      I'm the gingerbread man.'

And the horse could not catch him.
Perhaps no-one would ever catch him.

TRADITIONAL

The Jigsaw Puzzle

My beautiful picture of pirates and treasure
Is spoiled, and almost I don't want to start
To put it together; I've lost all the pleasure
I used to find in it: there's one missing part.

I know there's one missing — they lost it, the others,
The last time they played with my puzzle — and maybe
There's more than one missing: along with the brothers
And sisters who borrow my toys there's the baby.

There's a hole in the ship or the sea that it sails on,
And I said to my father, 'Well, what shall I do?,
It isn't the same now that some of it's gone.'
He said, 'Put it together; the world's like that too.'

RUSSELL HOBAN

31

A Good Play

We built a ship upon the stairs
All made of the back-bedroom chairs,
And filled it full of sofa pillows
To go a-sailing on the billows.

We took a saw and several nails,
And water in the nursery pails;
And Tom said, 'Let us also take
An apple and a slice of cake';
Which was enough for Tom and me
To go a-sailing on, till tea.

We sailed along for days and days,
And had the very best of plays;
But Tom fell out and hurt his knee,
So there was no one left but me.

ROBERT LOUIS STEVENSON

Dressing Up

Sally was wearing her long necklace of tinkling milk-bottle tops. She searched through the toy box and found her crown. Sally carefully put it on her head.

She had to hold it there to find the filmy scarf for her shoulders.

It very nearly slipped off as she foraged through boxes and toys and tins. Out came one silvery shoe! Out came another! She put her feet into her fancy dancing shoes. A moment later a very splendid Princess Sally clip-clopped most grandly through the door, on her way to a ball.

JEAN CHAPMAN

Susannah

Susannah put her apron on,
'I'm a witch, I'm a witch,' she said,
'And if you don't give me some diamonds,
I'll magic you into brown bread.
Who am I?' she asked her teddy.
'You're a witch, her teddy bear said.

Susannah put her slippers on,
'I'm a queen, I'm a queen,' she said
'And if you don't give me some rubies,
I'll chop all the curls off your head.
Who am I?' she asked her teddy.
'You're a queen,' her teddy bear said.

Susannah put her nightdress on
'I'm so tired, so tired,' she said.
Then she yawned and took out her ribbons
And snuggled down into her bed.
'Who am I?' she asked her teddy,
'Susannah,' her teddy bear said.

RICHARD EDWARDS

Knight-in-Armour

Whenever I'm a shining Knight,
I buckle on my armour tight;
And then I look about for things,
Like Rushings-out, and Rescuings,
And Savings from the Dragon's Lair,
And fighting all the Dragons there.
And sometimes when our fights begin,
I think I'll let the Dragons win ...
And then I think perhaps I won't,
Because they're Dragons, and I don't.

A. A. MILNE

from A Dragon's Bedtime

'Dad!' called Daryll. 'Mum! Come and see what I did! COME AND SEE!'

From far away, came a low, tremendous roar, like a growl of thunder. It was Daryll's dad, calling back to him, 'WE'RE COMING, DARYLL!'

Thump, thump. The earth was trembling with their running footsteps. Birds went squawking, and the sky was darkening.

And look! There was his great, green, wonderful, frightful mother — a vast and shining lady dragon, as big as a mountain. Behind her was his enormous dragon father — I can't begin to say how big HE was.

Daryll leaped up onto his mother's back. Together the three of them looked at what he had made — his swamp, his beautiful bay, his shining river.

'WELL DONE, MY LAD!' thundered Daryll's father. The three of them hugged each other, and Daryll's father thumped his scaly back.

'And NOW,' said Daryll's mother, 'bath — and bed!'

They bathed in the sea until they felt all clean and fresh.

JUDY HINDLEY

Dragon into Dressing Gown

I know a dragon dark and green —
He's quite the handsomest I've seen —
Who (sometimes less and sometimes more)
Lives just behind my bedroom door.

And (sometimes less but often more)
That dragon just behind the door
Rolls one eye up and one eye down
And turns into my dressing gown.

He doesn't do it in the night,
But in the early morning light
Where dragon was, there on its hook
That dressing gown gives me a look.

I've asked the dragon if he'd stay
And be a dragon through the day
But with a smile and with a frown
He turns into a dressing gown.

RUSSELL HOBAN

Grandpa Dropped His Glasses

Grandpa dropped his glasses once
In a pot of dye,
And when he put them on again
He saw a purple sky.
Purple birds were rising up
From a purple hill,
Men were grinding purple cider
At a purple mill.
Purple Adeline was playing
With a purple doll,
Little purple dragonflies
Were crawling up the wall.
And at the supper table
He got crazy as a loon
From eating purple apple dumplings
With a purple spoon.

LEROY F. JACKSON

35

from The Patchwork Quilt

Grandma's eyes grew dark and distant. She turned away from Tanya and gazed out of the window, absentmindedly rubbing the pieces of material through her fingers.

'Grandma, I'll help you make your quilt,' Tanya said.

'Thank you, honey.'

'Let's start right now. We'll be finished in no time.'

Grandma held Tanya close and patted her head. 'It's gonna take quite a while to make this quilt, not a couple of days or a week — not even a month. A good quilt, a masterpiece ...' Grandma's eyes shone at the thought. 'Why, I need more material. More gold and blue, some red and green. And I'll need the time to do it right. It'll take me a year at least.'

'A year!' shouted Tanya. 'That's too long. I can't wait that long, Grandma.'

Grandma laughed. 'A year ain't that long, honey. Makin' this quilt gonna be a joy. Now run along and let Grandma rest.' Grandma turned her head towards the sunlight and closed her eyes.

'I'm gonna make a masterpiece,' she murmured, clutching a scrap of cloth in her hand, just before she fell asleep.

VALERIE FLOURNOY

from A Lullaby for Freddie

Freddie the Fearless is a toy soldier, come to live in the doll's house.

FREDDIE:

I expect that all of you are longing to hear tales of my soldiering, my bravery, assorted sagas of fights and battles and so on, aren't you? I mean, this is an extremely pleasant doll's house, and they do say a change is as good as a rest, but it's not quite what I'm used to, oh no indeed! I lived in a fort — a splendid cardboard fort in the middle of a sandy desert. There were palm trees and camels and we had battles in the morning. In the afternoon we marched around and had parades, and in the evening we all lined up on the floor of the fort for a spot of shut-eye. Oh, those were the days! All the other soldiers are gone now. Gone! Every last one. Dropped behind chests of drawers, exchanged for cars and things, taken away and given to jumble sales if there was anything wrong with them at all, even the slightest scratch ... oh, there have been so many casualties!

ADÈLE GERAS

The Sad Story of a Little Boy that Cried

Once a little boy, Jack, was, oh! ever so good,
Till he took a strange notion to cry all he could.

So he cried all the day, and he cried all the night,
He cried in the morning and in the twilight;

He cried till his voice was as hoarse as a crow,
And his mouth grew so large it looked like a great O.

It grew at the bottom, and grew at the top;
It grew till they thought that it never would stop.

Each day his great mouth grew taller and taller,
And his dear little self grew smaller and smaller.

At last, that same mouth grew so big that — alack! —
It was only a mouth with a border of Jack.

ANONYMOUS

37

Night-Nursery Thoughts

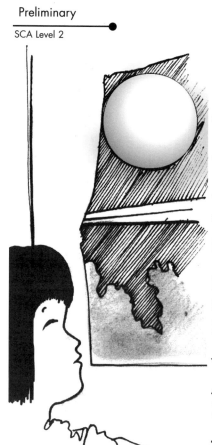

O sometimes when I wake at night
I think the moon so round and bright
That it must fall for very light.

That lovely, lovely liquid fall
Would make the stars cry out and call,
But would not burn my hands at all.

Now even raindrops off the tip
Of leaves and twigs, soft, softly drip;
But if the moon should suddenly slip,

You would not hear the softest sup
And nobody could scrape it up;
It could not stay in any cup.

The moon would fall without a sound
Without a stain upon the ground,
And in the morning not be found.

FRANCES CORNFORD

The White Window

The Moon comes every night to peep
Through the window where I lie:
But I pretend to be asleep;
And watch the Moon go slowly by,
— And she never makes a sound!

She stands and stares! And then she goes
To the house that's next to me,
Stealing by on tippy-toes;
To peep at folk asleep maybe
— And she never makes a sound!

JAMES STEPHENS

Bully Night

Bully night
I do not like
the company you keep
The burglars and the bogeymen
who slink
while others sleep

Bully night
I do not like
the noises that you make
The creaking and the shrieking
that keep me
fast awake.

Bully night
I do not like
the loneliness you bring
the loneliness you bring
The loneliness, the loneliness
the loneliness you bring,
the loneliness you bring
the loneliness, the

ROGER McGOUGH

From The Tidying Up of Thomas

Thomas was a rough, untidy child. His kind
uncles and aunts had given him a Noah's Ark
and a farm and a zoo and soldiers and cars
and games and paints and books and goldfish
and a rocking-horse and a blackboard and a
Red Indian costume and — oh, everything you
have ever wanted.

But he was so *rough*, and so *untidy*!

His poor mother was distracted. She didn't
know what to do about Thomas.

One day he fetched the scissors out of her
work-box and pulled all the stuffing out of poor
old Teddy. Teddy would have had to be thrown
away if Thomas's mother hadn't collected it and
sewn him up again.

'You're a very naughty, wasteful, silly little boy!' she scolded him, 'And you don't deserve all those lovely toys.'

Another day Thomas was playing in the kitchen while his mother was writing letters, and when she went in to make tea she found he had mixed up the sugar and the flour and the barley and the tea and he had broken the coffee-pot and spilt the vinegar.

'Oh Thomas, Thomas!' she cried, 'I only hope you're ashamed of yourself!'

But Thomas wasn't ashamed of himself, not in the least bit! He thought he was really very clever.

CHARLOTTE HOUGH

from Pinocchio

Pinocchio is on his way to school for the first time ...

PINOCCHIO:
At school today I shall learn to read in no time; tomorrow I shall learn to write and then, the day after tomorrow I shall learn how to add up and take away. Soon I will be clever enough to earn lots and lots of money, and with my very first money I shall buy Gepetto the best and warmest coat I can find, made of fine cloth. No. It won't be a cloth coat. It shall be made of gold and silver with sparkling diamond buttons. My poor Daddy deserves the best ... because he sold his coat to buy me this book for school ... and now he has no coat, and in this cold weather too! *(He hears some music playing and starts to dance along to it)* Dum-di-dum ... fi-fi-fi- ... Where is that music coming from, I wonder ... and who is playing? What a shame that I have to go to school ... Otherwise ... I know! Today I'll go and listen to the music and tomorrow I'll go to school! That's a good idea! *(He dances off, humming)*

CARLO COLLODI

from The Secret Garden

MARY: *(talking to Dickon)*

I don't know anything about boys. Could you keep a secret, if I told you one? It's a great secret. I don't know what I should do if anyone found it out. I believe I should die! I've stolen a garden. It isn't mine. It isn't anybody's. Nobody wants it, nobody cares for it, nobody ever goes into it. Perhaps everything is dead in it already; I don't know. I don't care, I don't care! Nobody has any right to take it from me when I care about it and they don't. They're letting it die, all shut in by itself. I've nothing to do. Nothing belongs to me. I found it myself and I got into it myself. I was only just like the robin, and they wouldn't take it from the robin. Come with me and I'll show you. It's this ... it's a secret garden, and I'm the only one in the world who wants it to be alive.

FRANCES HODGSON BURNETT

To Any Garden

Garden, grow,
In clump and row,
Golden trumpet, branch of snow,
Bell of blue and drop of white,
Swelling with your fill of light.

Garden, show your shades of green,
Spires of green, and blades of green
Crinkled leaves upon whose bed
Little yellow stars are spread.

Garden, grow,
Quick and slow,
Some surprise each morning show;
Lovely as your blue and gold,
Are the surprises you withhold.

ELEANOR FARJEON

Teddy Robinson goes up a Tree

Up and up went Teddy Robinson, higher and higher, and then — swish! — he fell right into the middle of the apple-tree. A sea of green leaves brushed his face as he began falling again, and then suddenly he stopped with a jerk and found himself sitting astride a branch.

The bird flew down beside him and began hopping up and down on the branch.

'Bounce a bit,' he said. 'It's quite fun, especially when the wind's blowing like it is now.'

'Ooo-err, look out!' said Teddy Robinson, as the branch waved up and down under him.

But it was all right. He seemed to be stuck quite firmly where he was, and after a while he stopped feeling wobbly, and began to enjoy himself instead.

'This is very jolly,' he said, bouncing a little higher. 'I've never been so high up in the world before. I should think I'm jolly nearly at the top of the tree. It's making me feel quite bouncy. I always knew I was a clever bear, but I'd no idea I was as clever as this, to be sitting right up here all by myself. Why, anybody'd think I'd climbed up here just for fun. What a very clever bear I are! It really is very jolly getting above myself like this.' And he began singing:

> 'Three cheers for me
> at the top of the tree,
> the cleverest bear you ever did see.
> Nobody knows
> how clever I are.
> Who would suppose
> I could climb so far?
> Three cheers for me
> at the top of the tree.
> Oh, what a wonderful bear I be!'

JOAN ROBINSON

from The Bear

TILLY:
Mummy! Mummy! Daddy!
I was woken up by a bear!
He licked my face with his tongue to wake me up.
It was ever so rough.
And he had great big black wet nostrils blowing hot air in my face.
It's true!
He wanted to be friendly!
You should see his teeth!
They're all yellow and enormous.
Longer than my fingers.
He's got real fangs.
I saw them when he yawned.
And his claws!
They're all black and curved like hooks.
He could easily tear me to bits and eat me.
He wouldn't though.
He really likes me. I can tell.
Can he stay, Mummy?
I want him to sleep with me. I won't need a duvet.
He's the cuddliest thing in the whole world ... *(reacting to her father)* You've got no fur, Daddy.
But you're quite nice.
I do still like you a little bit.

RAYMOND BRIGGS

The Dancing Bear

Slowly he turns himself round and round,
  Lifting his paws with care,
Twisting his head in a sort of bow
  To the people watching there.

His keeper, grinding a wheezy tune,
  Jerks at the iron chain,
And the dusty, patient bear goes through
  His solemn tricks again.

Only his eyes are still and fixed
  In a wide, bewildered stare,
More like a child's lost in woods at night
  Than the eyes of a big brown bear.

RACHEL FIELD

from Jesus' Christmas Party

There was nothing the innkeeper liked more than
a good night's sleep.
But that night there was a knock at the door.
'No room,' said the innkeeper.
'But we're tired and have travelled through night
and day.'
'There's only the stable round the back. Here's two
blankets. Sign the register.'
So they signed it: 'Mary and Joseph'.
Then he shut the door, climbed the stairs, got into bed
and went to sleep.
But then, later, there was another knock at the door.
'Excuse me. I wonder if you could lend us another,
smaller blanket?'

'There. One smaller blanket,' said the innkeeper.
Then he shut the door, climbed the stairs, got into bed, and went to sleep.
But then a bright light woke him up.
'That's ALL I need,' said the innkeeper.
Then he shut the door, climbed the stairs, drew the curtains, got into bed, and went to sleep.
But then there was ANOTHER knock at the door.
'We are three shepherds.'
'Well, what's the matter? Lost your sheep?'
'We've come to see Mary and Joseph.'
'ROUND THE BACK,' said the innkeeper.
Then he shut the door, climbed the stairs, got into bed, and went to sleep.
But then there was yet ANOTHER knock at the door.
'We are three kings. We've come ...'
'ROUND THE BACK!'

NICHOLAS ALLAN

Tonio's Gift

Five-year-old Tonio was chosen to be the youngest shepherd in the Nativity play. The children were asked to bring a present for the babe in the manger. Tonio, whose family was very poor, brought his most precious possession, a piece of wood, worn smooth with handling. It was his only toy, which he had kept hidden and played with in secret, otherwise it would have been taken from him and used for fire-wood. He wept a little as he parted with it.

A visitor, hearing the story of his gift, sent a beautiful red engine to Tonio in place of his piece of wood. Beaming with delight, Tonio tip-toed to the crib and retrieved his piece of wood, leaving the beautiful red engine in its place.

ANONYMOUS

Icicle Joe

I made a snowman:
Icicle Joe.
The moon shone round him
high and low ...
The moon shone round him
sides and back —
it gave him a shadow,
purple-black.

I made a snowman
white and plump;
a nose he had
like a sugar lump.
The sun shone round him ...
One bright day
he slumped a little
and went away,

Vanishing softly
bit by bit
like a lollipop does
when you suck at it.
Only a puddle
stayed to show
where I had built him —
Icicle Joe.

JEAN KENWARD

A Dark Dark Tale

Once upon a time there was a dark, dark moor.
On the moor there was a dark, dark wood.
In the wood there was a dark, dark house.
At the front of the house there was a dark, dark door.
Behind the door there was a dark, dark hall.
In the hall there were some dark, dark stairs.
Up the stairs there was a dark, dark passage.
Across the passage was a dark, dark curtain.
Behind the curtain was a dark, dark room.
In the room was a dark, dark cupboard.
In the cupboard was a dark, dark corner.
In the corner was a dark, dark box.
And in the box there was ... A MOUSE!

RUTH BROWN

Hickory, Dickory, Dock

Hickory, Dickory, Dock,
The mouse ran down the clock —
She had watched the cat go out of the door,
She saw some crumbs on the kitchen floor,
And she gobbled them up — Tick-tock!

Hickory, Dickory, Dock,
The mouse ran up the clock —
For she heard the stealthy tread of the cat,
And she didn't care to stay after that,
So she scampered back — Tick-tock!

Hickory, Dickory, Dock,
The mouse slept in the clock —
But when she awoke, she gnawed her way
Through the old clock-case one winter day,
And never came back — Tick-tock!

ANONYMOUS

He was a Rat, and She was a Rat

He was a rat, and she was a rat,
  And down in one hole they did dwell,
And both were as black as a witch's cat,
  And they loved each other well.

He had a tail, and she had a tail,
  Both long and curling and fine:
And each said, 'Yours is the finest tail
  In the world, excepting mine.'

He smelt the cheese, and she smelt the cheese,
  And they both pronounced it good;
And both remarked it would greatly add
  To the charms of their daily food.

So he ventured out, and she ventured out,
  And I saw them go with pain;
But what befell them I never can tell,
  For they never came back again.

ANONYMOUS

The Piper

Piping down the valleys wild,
   Piping songs of pleasant glee,
On a cloud I saw a child,
   And he laughing said to me:

'Pipe a song about a Lamb!'
   So I piped with merry cheer.
'Piper, pipe that song again';
   So I piped: he wept to hear.

'Drop thy pipe, thy happy pipe;
   Sing thy songs of happy cheer!'
So I sang the same again,
   While he wept with joy to hear.

'Piper, sit thee down and write
   In a book that all may read.'
So he vanish'd from my sight,
   And I pluck'd a hollow reed,

And I made a rural pen,
   And I stain'd the water clear,
And I wrote my happy songs
   Every child may joy to hear.

WILLIAM BLAKE

from Worzel Gummidge

WORZEL GUMMIDGE: *(talking to Susan)*
Gummidge. I'm Worzel Gummidge. I chose the name this morning. My granfer's name was Bogle ... How old am I? ... All manner of ages. My face is one age, and my feet are another, and my arms are the oldest of all ... 'Tis usual with scarecrows. And it's a good way too. I get a lot of birthdays. One for my face and another for my middle and another for my hands and so on ... I've never walked about before. But I says to myself last night, when I was standing in Ten-acre Field, I says to myself 'You ought to go about the world and see things, same as the rabbits do. What's the use of having smart legs if you don't use them?' ... I thought I'd go to London, till I met a mouse in the lane and she changed my mind for me ... She had been to London herself. She was a field mouse and she'd heard tell of stowaways. So she stowed herself away in a market basket and she saw Piccadilly ... she saw a policeman and he was dressed just the same as the one in Scatterbrook, and she said if they couldn't do better than that in Piccadilly, she'd come home again. And she said they told such lies. There's a place they call St Martin in the Fields, and it isn't in the fields at all. There's another place called Shepherd's Market, and she said there wasn't a shepherd there. So she said London was all a sham, and that it was trying to
copy Scatterbrook, so she came home again ...
And I've come here to fetch my umbrella.

BARBARA EUPHAN TODD

Allie

'Allie, call the birds in,
The birds from the sky.'
Allie calls, Allie sings,
Down they all fly.
First there came
Two white doves
Then a sparrow from his nest,
Then a clucking bantam hen,
Then a robin red-breast.

'Allie, call the beasts in,
The beasts, every one.'
Allie calls, Allie sings,
In they all run.
First there came
Two black lambs,
Then a grunting Berkshire sow,
Then a dog without a tail,
Then a red and white cow.

'Allie, call the fish up,
The fish from the stream.'
Allie calls, Allie sings,
Up they all swim.
First there came
Two gold fish,
A minnow and a miller's thumb,
Then a pair of loving trout,
Then the twisted eels come.

'Allie, call the children,
Children from the green.'
Allie calls, Allie sings,
Soon they run in.
First there came
Tom and Madge,
Kate and I who'll not forget
How we played by the water's edge
Till the April sun set.

ROBERT GRAVES

51

Nix Nought Nothing

Mary kneels at the front of the stage, looking intently downwards, and reaching down her white palms as if to the brink of the lake.

MARY: Oh fish, oh fish,
I am the wizard's daughter,
So give me my wish:
Out of the world of weeds and water.
Twining, shining, slithering stalks,
Dark green buds of the water lily
Under the water spider's walks,
Softest slime where the bright and chilly
Eels go turning, with great tails churning
Rotted leaves into floating scum,
Out of the glistening deeps, oh listening
Thousands — myriads — fishes, come!

Fish, fish, you that know me,
Dimly shimmering fins below me,
Thirsty throats that no draught can slake,
Go and drain me my father's lake!
Goggle-eyes, off,
Make no long stop of it,
Drink every drop of it!
All to be done
By set of sun,
Quick, away, be it well begun!

(She makes a great sweep with her hands, outwards and downwards.)

NAOMI MITCHISON

JOSEPH:

Can't you recognize my face? Is it hard to see
That Joseph who you thought was dead — your brother — is me?
I closed my eyes, drew back the curtain
To see for certain what I thought I knew
Far far away someone was weeping
But the world was sleeping, any dream will do
I wore my coat with golden lining
Bright colours shining, wonderful and new
And in the east the dawn was breaking
And the world was waking, any dream will do
A crash of drums, a flash of light
My golden coat flew out of sight
The colours faded into darkness, I was left alone
May I return to the beginning
The light is dimming and the dream is too
The world and I, we are still waiting
Still hesitating, any dream will do
Give me my coloured coat, my amazing coloured coat
Give me my coloured coat, my amazing coloured coat

from Joseph and the Amazing Technicolor Dreamcoat

TIM RICE

One Spring Day

Melanie, Melanie Wilberforce
Knows just how it feels
To clatter along the garden path
In her mam's high heels.

Baby brother, Charlie,
Is snoozing in his pram
Underneath the washing line
Just like a little lamb.

Clatter, crunch, clatter,
Those spiky heels go,
Crunch, scrape, clatter, clack …
Little does she know

That Charlie's going to wake and bawl
Any minute now
And mum is going to dash outside
And make poor Melanie howl.

But until that awful moment comes
Let little Charlie snooze
And Melanie scrape the concrete
In her mam's best shoes.

This world is full of trouble,
So let the baby snore
And Melanie go clattering
Half a minute more.

MATT SIMPSON

Taking Out Jim

We left the dusty
Road and wheeled
The push-chair straight
Into the field;
So thick the dande-
lions grew,
We thought we'd deck
The baby too.

So standing in
A circle round him,
With Linda's straw
School-hat we crowned him;
Stuck dandelions
Round the band,
And squeezed a big one
In his hand.

With dandelion-
Chains a-swinging,
We sang his praise
In softest singing;
We called him Dande-
lion Jim,
And pelted him,
And tickled him.

Half-smothered under
Linda's hat,
All giggling
And plump he sat,
A pollen-patch
Upon his nose,
And juice-stains down
His new white blouse.

Then, overcome
By sudden fears,
We brushed the petals
From his ears,
Straightened his hair
With Beryl's comb,
And thought we'd better
Take him home.

JOHN WALSH

Brother

I had a little brother
And I brought him to my mother
And I said I want another
Little brother for a change.
But she said don't be a bother
So I took him to my father
And I said this little bother
Of a brother's very strange.

But he said one little brother
Is exactly like another
And every little brother
Misbehaves a bit he said.
So I took the little brother
From my mother and my father
And I put the little bother
Of a brother back to bed.

MARY ANN HOBERMAN

from Rebecca of Sunnybrook Farm

Jeremiah Cobb is driving Rebecca to her aunt's house and on the drive she tells him all about her family ... they are in a stage-coach, horse-driven. Time: Late 19th Century. Rebecca is about 10.

REBECCA: There are seven children in our family, Mr Cobb. Seven. There's verses written about seven children:

Quick was the little maid's reply —
'O master, we are seven!'

I learned it to speak in school, but the scholars were hateful and laughed. Hannah is the oldest; I come next, then John, then Jenny, then Mark, then Fanny, then Mira.

My mother's name is Aurelia Randall. Our names are Hannah Lucy Randall, Rebecca Rowena Randall, John Halifax Randall, Jenny Lind Randall, Marquis Randall, Fanny Ellsler Randall, and Miranda Randall. Mother named half of us and father the other half; but we didn't come out even, so they both thought it would be nice to name Mira after Aunt Miranda, in Riverboro. They hoped it might do some good; but it didn't, and now we call her Mira. We are all named after somebody in particular. Hannah is Hannah at the Window Binding Shoes, and I am taken out of *Ivanhoe*; John Halifax was a gentleman in a book; Mark is after his uncle, Marquis de Lafayette, that died a twin. Twins very often don't live to grow up, and triplets almost never. Did you know that, Mr Cobb ? We don't call him Marquis, only Mark. Jenny is named for a singer and Fanny for a beautiful dancer; but mother says they're both misfits, for Jenny can't carry a tune, and Fanny's kind of stiff-legged. Mother would like to call them Jane and Frances and give up their middle names, but she says it wouldn't be fair to father. She says we must always stand up for father, because everything was against him, and he wouldn't have died if he hadn't had such bad luck. I think that's all there is to tell about us.

KATE DOUGLAS WIGGIN

55

from Curtain Up

MIRIAM:

Which is my cousin Holly ? ...

We're cousins. I'm Miriam Cohen. You're just a tiny bit older than me ... Let's be friends. Mum says if we're friends I can ask you to tea. I can't come to you because we're not on speaking terms with Grandmother just now. We hardly ever are, you know, except at Christmas. Of course, we always go to Grandmother's then.

Mum's made me two tunics and two knickers. She cut up one of her best nightdresses. I think that was pretty decent of her, don't you ? She said I'd have to have two. She knew I wouldn't be clean a minute if I only had one. I've got the locker next to you, Holly, they told me so at the door ...

I began tap when I was three, then I started acrobatic work, you know, flip flaps and all that. I learnt to sing when I was four. I did some shows with Dad for charity when I was five. I don't really ever remember a time when I wasn't learning, but mostly I went to special classes or learnt at home. That's why they've sent me here. It's to see which way I'm heading — at least, that's what Dad says. He thinks it's time I specialised. He says I'm too plain for the glamour type and I ought to do a lot of acrobatic work and become a comedienne. But I shan't, I'm going to dance. He knows that really. There's no doubt about it, I'm a bitter disappointment.

NOEL STREATFEILD

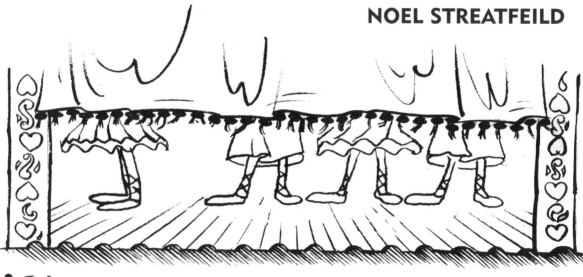

The Song of Tilly Lally

O, I say, you Joe,
Throw us the ball!
I've a good mind to go
And leave you all.
I never saw such a bowler
To bowl the ball in a tansy
And clean it with my hankercher
Without saying a word.

That Bill's a foolish fellow;
He has given me a black eye.
He does not know how to handle a bat
Any more than a dog or a cat;
He has knock'd down the wicket,
And broke the stumps,
And runs without shoes to save his pumps.

WILLIAM BLAKE

from Lost – One Pair of Legs

'Hey!' bawled Cal in horror. 'Come back! Come back! You're
my leg! You've no right to go off and leave me in the lurch.
And that isn't the right bus!'

Lurch was the right word. With only one leg, Cal was
swaying about like a hollyhock in a gale. He was obliged to
prop himself up with his tennis racket. He turned angrily to the
lady and said, 'Did *you* do that ? You've no right to take away
my leg! It isn't fair!'

'Nothing is fair,' said the lady sternly. 'What you did to my
butterfly was not fair either. You may think yourself lucky I
didn't take the other leg as well.'

'I think you are a mean old witch!' said Cal.

Instantly he felt a jerk as his left leg undid itself from the hip. Cal bumped down on to the grass, hard, while his left leg went capering away across the grass, free as you please, up on the point of its toe, pirouetting like a ballerina. When it reached the bus stop a number 16 had just pulled up; the left leg hopped nimbly on board and was carried away.

'You're on the wrong bus! Come back!' shouted Cal, but the leg made no answer to that.

JOAN AIKEN

There Was an Old Woman

There was an old woman of Chester-le-Street
Who chased a policeman all over his beat.

She shattered his helmet and tattered his clothes
And knocked his new spectacles clean off his nose.

'I'm afraid,' said the Judge, 'I must make it quite clear
You can't get away with that sort of thing here.'

'I can and I will,' the old woman she said,
'And I don't give a fig for your water and bread.

I don't give a hoot for your cold prison cell,
And your bolts and your bars and your handcuffs as well.

I've never been one to do just as I'm bid.
You can put me in jail for a year!'
                                        So they did.

CHARLES CAUSLEY

There was a naughty boy
        And a naughty boy was he,
For nothing would he do
        But scribble poetry —

*from
A Song
of Myself*

He took
An ink stand
In his hand
And a pen
Big as ten
In the other
And away
In a Pother
He ran
To the mountains
And fountains
And ghostes
And Postes
And witches
And ditches
And wrote
In his coat
When the weather
Was cool,
Fear of gout,
And without
When the weather
Was warm —
Och the charm
When we choose
To follow one's nose

To the north,
To the north,
To follow one's nose
To the north!

JOHN KEATS

from The Princess and the Pea

There was once a prince who wished to marry a princess — but a real princess she had to be. So he travelled all the world over to find one; yet in every case something was wrong. At last he came back home, quite downhearted, for he did so want to have a real princess.

One evening there was a fearful storm; thunder raged, lightning flashed, rain poured down in torrents — it was terrifying. In the midst of it all, someone knocked at the palace door, and the old King went to open it.

Standing there was a princess. But, goodness! What a state she was in! The water ran down her hair and her clothes, through the tips of her shoes and out at the heels. Still, she *said* she was a real princess.

'Well, we'll find out soon enough,' the old Queen thought. She didn't say a word, though, but went into the spare bedroom, took off all the bedclothes, and laid a little pea on the mattress. Then she piled up twenty more mattresses on top of it, and twenty eiderdowns over that. There the Princess was to sleep that night.

When morning came, they asked her how she had slept.

'Oh, shockingly! Not a wink of sleep the whole night long! Heaven knows what was in the bed, but I lay on something hard that has made me black and blue all over. It was quite dreadful.'

Now they were sure that here was a real princess, since she had felt the pea through twenty eiderdowns and twenty mattresses. Only a real princess could be so sensitive.

So the Prince married her; no need to search any further. The pea was put in the museum; you can go and see it for yourself if no one has taken it.

There's a fine story for you!

HANS ANDERSEN
Translated by NAOMI LEWIS

Her Majesty went softly
To make the stranger's bed,
And took a crumpled rose-leaf
A leaf of old Jacqueminot,
Of scented sweet Jacqueminot,
    And shook a cunning head.
She hid it in the mattress,
    And over it she spread
Forty layers of swan's down,
And twenty quilts of goose's down,
And shook them up and shook them down,
    To make them light, she said.

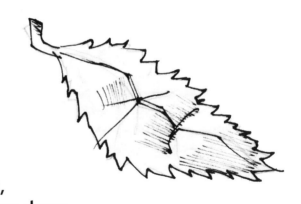

She laid upon this mountain
    Her sheets of finest thread,
And three-and-thirty blankets,
The whitest Witney blankets
From all the thickest fleeces,
    The land of Sussex bred;
And over that a cover
    That fragrant odours shed,
Above the snowy pillows,
The lightest puffy pillows,
The softest pillows ever known;
    To make her sleep, she said.

The Crumpled Rose-Leaf and The Real Princess

The Queen came in next morning:
    'How did you rest?' she said.
The stranger told her sadly,
And showed a host of bruises,
Across her slender shoulders
    And down her back they spread
Like petals of Jacqueminot
    So satin-soft and red.
She wept, the weary Princess:
'Oh, oh! I am so sleepy!
I wish I hadn't stayed with you,
    It's such a horrid bed!'

ELIZABETH FLEMING

61

from The Toymaker

Once upon a time there was a toymaker called Matthew.
He loved making toys. He worked hard all day long tap-tap-tapping
and stitch-stitch-stitching. He sold the toys he made to people who
came to his shop, so that he could make money to keep himself and
his daughter, Mary.
Mary was not strong.
She could not go out to play with the other children.
She stayed inside and watched them through the shop window.
Sometimes she was lonely.
Matthew wanted to make her happy so he made her special toys.
They were dolls.
He made them very carefully so that each doll looked like one of the
children who played outside the shop window.
Mary played with the dolls.
She called them Max and Lily and Bertie, after the children outside.
They made her happy.
Because she was happy she grew stronger.
At last she was able to go outside to play.
She played and she played and she played.
The dolls sat in the shop window, watching,
Matthew watched too, as he worked.
He smiled when she laughed because he loved her.
No one played with the dolls any more.
Matthew thought that Mary had forgotten them.
He put them safely on a shelf at the back of the shop.
People saw the dolls and asked, 'How much is this one?' But
Matthew said; 'They are not for sale. They belong to Mary.'
He would not sell the dolls, not a single one, for they were his
memories and they kept him company.

MARTIN WADDELL

from Teddy Bear's Picnic

Tran, a toy robot of the sharp brainy gangster type and LCD, another robot, are victimising the traditional toys.

TRAN: *(listening)* **Hey, there's someone else in the toy box. That'll be the panda and rabbit he was telling us about. Hey, panda and rabbit I know you're in there. I can hear you creeping about. Now hear this! We've just dealt with Action Man and Teddy Bear. When you come out we're gonna deal with you. Understand?**

You see it's like this, Action Man, you and your kind are finished. All the toys of your generation — the pretend generation — are obsolete. You have been superseded by the new order of toys. We are the toys of the future. We are electronic. We have computers — computers that will do away with the need to pretend. And from this moment we are in charge. Let me give you my vision of the nurseries of the future. I can see it all now — they will be full of electronic toys. Toys that will work entirely on their own. The whole floor will be busy with automated cars running around and robots walking and talking. There'll be video games so advanced that they won't need anyone to play them, they play themselves. It'll be a computerized play environment. Children won't need to do a thing. All they'll have to do is to sit and watch. They won't even need to switch anything on, that'll be automatic as well. That is how it will be. In the meantime, 'til you finally get the push, you will obey us. OK, you two — stay where you are and keep quiet. We've got things to decide and plans to make. And we don't want you listening in!

PAUL KING

63

from *The Indian in the Cupboard*

OMRI: *(talking to his friend Patrick)*
Little Bull isn't a toy. He's a real man. He really
lived. Maybe he's still — I don't know — he's in
the middle of his life — somewhere in America in
seventeen something-or-other. He's from the *past.*

Listen. Little Bull has told me about his life. He's
fought in wars, and scalped people, and grown
stuff to eat like marrows and stuff, and had a wife.
She died. He doesn't know how he got here but he
thinks it's magic and he accepts magic, he believes
in it, he thinks I'm some kind of spirit or something.
What I mean, is that if you put all those men in
there, when they came to life they'd be real men
with real lives of their own, from their own times and
countries, talking their own languages. You couldn't
just — set them up and make them do what you wanted
them to. They'd do what *they* wanted to, or they might get terrified
and run away or — well, one I tried it with, an old Indian, actually
died of — of fright. When he saw me. Look, if you don't believe me!
(He opens the cupboard).

LYNNE REID BANKS

Making My First Snowman In My Mother's Pink Rubber Gloves

I scooped and shaped him lovingly,
I piled and patted best as could be,
though my pink hands were burning me,
I kept on building my first snowman.

I shaped his shoulders and fixed his neck,
I smooth his face and rounded his head,
though my pink hands were freezing me,
I kept on building my first snowman.

I put the usual carrot in, for the nose,
a banana for a mouth, my two best conkers for his eyes,
though my pink hands were killing me,
I kept on building my first snowman.

I threw my Dad's black jacket
to keep the cold from his back,
I stuck on his head the old felt hat,
then I stepped back.

Why was he staring at me with those big eyes?
Why was he so freezingly alive?
Man, why was he looking at me so?
                    Oh, No,

He wasn't a snowman.
HE WAS A SNOWCROW!

GRACE NICHOLS

from Aunt Arabelle in Charge

William Brown and friends have met a small boy in the village ...

ANTHONY MARTIN:
   I'm Anthony Martin ... Don't you know Anthony Martin? ... **Good
heavens! Whatever sort of books do you read?** *(reacts to William's
choice)* **Good heavens! I shouldn't have thought there was** *anyone* —
Haven't you read any of the Anthony Martin books? My mother writes
them, but they're about me. Poems and stories. All about me. Nearly
half a million copies have been sold, and they've been translated into
fourteen different languages. I've had my photograph in literally
hundreds of papers. *Good* papers, I mean. Not rubbish. They're *literary*
stories and poems, you know. Really cultured people buy them for their
children. There were several Anthony Martin parties in London last
year. *Hundreds* of children came. Just to see me. Have you *really* never
heard of me? You can't know much about *books*, then, and your

65

people can't either, or they'd have bought them for you. They're *the* children's classic nowadays. I have *hundreds* of letters from people who've read them. People I've never met. They send me presents at Christmas, too. I simply can't understand your never having heard of me. Good morning.

RICHMAL CROMPTON

from The Sea of Tranquillity

Years ago there was a little boy who had the solar system on his wall.

Late at night he'd lie in bed with Rabbit and they'd watch the planets spinning round the sun: Mars, the tiny space-tomato, Saturn sitting in its Frisbee rings, freezing Pluto, turning slowly in the dark, Jupiter, Uranus, Neptune, Venus, Mercury and Earth.

But of all the weird worlds that whirled across his bedroom wall, his favourite was the moon, a small and bald and ordinary globe of rock that loop-the-looped its way through outer space.

He leant across the windowsill at night and watched the moon slide up into the sky above the biscuit factory.

He borrowed Dad's binoculars and gazed for hours at the empty deserts and the rocky mountains.

And it made him dizzy just to think that he was looking at another world two hundred thousand miles away.

He got an atlas of the moon for Christmas and he read it like a storybook.

MARK HADDON

from The Story of Holly and Ivy

When Mr Jones and Ivy came in Mrs Jones was in the kitchen with a fork in her hand, turning the sausages. Mr Jones told Ivy to wait in the hall.

'Merry Christmas,' said Mr Jones to Mrs Jones and kissed her.

'Merry Christmas,' said Mrs Jones, but she sounded a little sad.

Mr Jones had a present in his pocket for Mrs Jones, a little gold brooch. He took it out, unwrapped it, and pinned it to her dress. 'Oh, how pretty, Albert!' said Mrs Jones, but she still sounded sad.

'I have another Christmas present for you,' said Mr Jones and laughed. 'It has two legs,' said Mr Jones.

'Two legs?' asked Mrs Jones, and Mr Jones laughed again.

'It can walk and talk,' said Mr Jones and laughed still more, and then he brought Ivy in.

When Mrs Jones saw Ivy she did not laugh; for a moment she stood still, then she dropped the fork and knelt down on the floor and put her hands on Ivy's shoulders. 'Oh, Albert!' said Mrs Jones. 'Albert!' She looked at Ivy for a long time and tears came into her eyes and rolled down her cheeks. Ivy, with her glove, wiped the tears away and the emptiness went out of Ivy and never came back.

'Dearie me!' said Mrs Jones, getting to her feet, 'what am I thinking of? You must have a hot bath at once.'

'Breakfast first,' said Mr Jones, and Ivy asked, 'Couldn't I see my Christmas tree?'

RUMER GODDEN

How the Fir Tree became our Christmas Tree

When the Christ Child was born, all people and animals, and even the trees, felt a great happiness.

Outside the stable where the Baby was lying, there stood three trees, a Palm tree, an Olive tree and a little Fir tree. Each day people passed beneath them bringing presents to the Baby.

'We should like to give him presents too,' said the trees.

'I shall give him my biggest leaf,' said the tall Palm tree. 'When the hot weather comes, it will fan him and bring cool breezes.'

Said the Olive tree: 'I will give him sweet-smelling oil.'

'But what can I give him ?' asked the little Fir tree anxiously.

'You! Your branches are prickly and your tears are sticky', said the other trees. 'You have nothing to give him.'

The little Fir tree was very sad. He tried hard to think of something he could give that the Christ Child might like, but he had nothing good enough.

Now an Angel had heard everything the trees had said and he was sorry for the little Fir tree. The stars were shining in the night sky, so, very gently, the Angel brought down some of the smallest and brightest of them and put them on the prickly branches of the Fir tree.

Inside the stable, the Baby was lying awake. He could see the three trees against the night sky. Suddenly the dark green branches of the little Fir tree shone and sparkled, for the stars were resting there like candles. How beautiful the little Fir tree seemed now!

And the Christ Child waved his hands, as babies do, and smiled.

And ever since the Fir tree has been the children's Christmas tree.

TRADITIONAL

Looking-Glass River

Smooth it slides upon its travel,
   Here a wimple, there a gleam —
      O the clean gravel!
      O the smooth stream!

Sailing blossoms, silver fishes,
   Paven pools as clear as air —
      How a child wishes
      To live down there!

We can see our coloured faces
   Floating on the shaken pool
      Down in cool places,
      Dim and very cool;

Till a wind or water wrinkle,
   Dipping marten, plumping trout,
      Spreads in a twinkle
      And blots all out.

See the rings pursue each other;
   All below grows black as night,
      Just as if mother
      Had blown out the light!

Patience, children, just a minute —
   See the spreading circles die;
      The stream and all in it
      Will clear by-and-by.

**ROBERT LOUIS
STEVENSON**

Bad Luck, Dead Duck

Lying there amongst the muck
Bad luck, dead duck;
Oil pollutes your river bed
How sad, too bad;
Lying still among the reeds,
Squelching mud and dead seeds,
Birds expire and fishes wheeze;
Bad luck, dead duck.

Oil has seeped into your lungs,
Bad luck, dead duck;
A short, short life was all you had;
How sad, too bad;
Lying dead; nobody cares,
Bad luck, dead duck.

No two feet of 'Aussie' soil,
Bad luck, dead duck;
To reward you for your toil;
How sad, too bad;
As you lie between the weeds;
No one cares; no one sees;
You'll lie there for years and years;
Bad luck, dead duck.

NICHOLAS DAVEY

69

from The Mouse and His Child

MISS MUDD: *(who is something like a small misshapen grasshopper, drab and muddy as her name)*
Maybe I could help you look, and maybe you'd talk to me and not eat me up. Would you, do you think, not eat me ? ... I'm here, by your feet. I don't have anyone to talk to. It's depressing ... I don't know who I am ... I don't even know WHAT I am. When I talk to myself I call myself Mudd. That's silly, I know, but you have to call yourself something if you've got no one else to talk to ... It's MISS Mudd ... and I'll be your friend if you'll be mine. Will you, do you think ? I'm so unsure of everything ... It's all so difficult. And of course everyone bigger than I tries to eat me, and I'm always busy eating everyone smaller. So there isn't much time to think things out. *(flings out an arm from her face, catches a water flea and eats it up)* ... It's distasteful, I know it's distasteful. I've got this nasty sort of huge lip with a joint in it like an elbow, and I catch my food with it. And the odd thing you see, is that I don't think that's how I really am. I just can't believe that I'm this muddy thing you see crawling about in the muck. I don't FEEL as if I am. I simply can't tell you how I feel inside! Clean and bright and beautiful ... like a song in the sunlight, like a sigh in the summer air. Do you ever feel that way ?

RUSSELL HOBAN

from A Dog So Small

Then, suddenly, when Ben could hardly see, he saw clearly. He saw clearly that you couldn't have impossible things, however much you wanted them. He saw that if you didn't have the possible things, then you had nothing. At the same time Ben remembered other things about the brown dog besides its unChiquitito-like size and colour and timidity. He remembered the warmth of the dog's body against his own, as he had carried him; and the movement of his body as he breathed; and the tickle of his curly hair; and the way the dog had pressed up to him for protection and had followed him even in hopelessness.

The brown dog had gone farther off now, losing himself in dusk. Ben could not see him any longer. He stood up; he peered over the Heath. No ...

Suddenly knowing what he had lost — whom he had lost, Ben shouted, 'Brown!'

He heard the dog's answering barks, even before he could see him. The dog was galloping towards him out of the dusk, but Ben went on calling: 'BrownBrownBrownBrown!'

Brown dashed up to him, barking so shrilly that Ben had to crouch down and, with the dog's tongue slapping all over his face, put his arms round him and said steadyingly, 'It's all right, Brown! Quiet, quiet! I'm here!'

Then Ben stood up again, and Brown remained by his side, leaning against his leg, panting, loving him; and lovingly Ben said, 'It's late, Brown. Let's go home.'

PHILIPPA PEARCE

71

from Hide and Shriek

Sophie stood alone in the mist. She was cold and frightened. She looked around desperately but Meg was nowhere to be seen.

Then she saw a tree. At least she thought it was a tree. But the tree began to move. The branches first. They moved in the way branches move when there is a strong gust of wind. The trouble was, there was no wind! Then the trunk of the tree began to move and as it moved it turned its face towards Sophie and its eyes were deep dark shadows and it smiled a hideous smile ...

Now, as you and I know perfectly well, trees have neither faces nor eyes, and as for trees smiling, well ... it's completely ridiculous, and this is exactly what Sophie was thinking when the tree threw back its head, and shouted in a horrible ghoulish voice, that was all too familiar to Sophie:

YOU CAN'T HIDE FROM ME!
NOBODY CAN HIDE FROM ME!

She ran.

But running through the mist in the dark is not easy. Things, as I have said before, suddenly appear. Things that weren't there suddenly are there.

And Sophie crashed into all of them.

PAUL DOWLING

from The Nearly Ghost Baby

People say they *nearly died of fright* and I honestly thought I would. I kept saying to myself through chattering teeth, 'Ghosts don't move chairs. They can just come *through* closed doors.'

But the chair fell over and the door swung open with its usual C-R-E-E-A-K. A cold, strong draught blew in. I could feel the coldness even though I had buried myself under the bedclothes.

I wanted to scream, I wanted to shout to Carey to wake up. I wanted to run to Mum and Dad. But I couldn't move. I couldn't make a sound. I was stiff — petrified! The only thing I didn't want to do was *look*.

Something was in the room, I knew it.

Was it the *thing* that lurked in the stairway down to the cave ?

From under the duvet, I heard the door open on to the landing at the other end of the room. And I heard a great sigh, only it was more like a sob this time. I thought, I'll never move again. I'll stay perfectly still until morning when Mum comes in. Then I heard Brian cry:

'WAGH - WAGH - WAGH - WAGH'

Suddenly it flashed into my mind — the old man in the Post Office saying: 'MIND THE GHOST DON'T GET HIM!'...

DELIA HUDDY

I am a Ghost who's lost his Boo

I am a ghost who's lost his boo,
my boo is gone from me,
and I'm without a single clue
to where my boo might be.
It makes me mope, it makes me pout,
it almost makes me moan,
a ghost is not a ghost without
a boo to call his own.

My boo was piercing, fierce, and loud,
I used to strut and boast,
for I was positively proud
to be a gruesome ghost.
But now that I'm without a boo,
I find it rather weird,
there's little for a ghost to do
whose boo has disappeared.

Although I hover here and there,
and haunt a hundred rooms,
it seems there's no one I can scare
unless my boo resumes.
I am a ghost who's lost his boo,
alas! A boo I lack,
if you should find my boo, then you
had better give it back.

JACK PRELUTSKY

73

I've never seen the Milkman

I've never seen the milkman,
His shiny cap or coat.
I've never seen him driving
His all-electric float.

When he comes by the morning's
As black as printers' ink.
I've never heard his footstep
Nor a single bottle clink.

No matter if it's foggy
Or snow is on the ground,
Or rain or hail or half a gale
He always does his round.

I wonder if he's thin or fat
Or fair or dark or bald,
Or short or tall, and most of all
I wonder what he's called.

He goes to bed so early
That not an owl has stirred,
And rises up again before
The earliest early bird.

God bless the faithful milkman,
My hero — and that's flat!
Or perhaps he's a milklady ?
(I never thought of that.)

CHARLES CAUSLEY

Cobweb Morning

On a Monday morning
We do spellings and Maths.
And silent reading.

But on the Monday
After the frost
We went straight outside.

Cobwebs hung in the cold air,
Everywhere.
All around the playground,
They clothed the trees,
Dressed every bush
In veils of fine white lace.

Each web,
A wheel of patient spinning.
Each spider,
Hidden,
Waiting.

Inside,
We worked all morning
To capture the outside.

Now
In our patterns and poems
We remember
The cobweb morning.

JUNE CREBBIN

from The Mousehole Cat

Then one year there came a terrible winter. At the far end of England the blue-green sea turned grey and black.

The Great Storm-Cat is stirring, thought Mowzer as she watched at her window. The wind whined like a wild thing about the high headlands. It came hunting the fishing boats in their hidden harbours. When the Great Storm-Cat is howling, thought Mowzer, it is best to stay snug indoors by a friendly fire.

The sea drew itself up into giant waves and flung itself against the great breakwaters. All along the coast of Cornwall, the stone walls stood the shock.

Then the sea sucked up its strength again and roared right over them, sinking the sailing boats in their home havens. But it could not get into the Mousehole.

Mowzer watched as the Great Storm-Cat clawed with his giant cat's paw through the gap in the harbour wall. But it was too small.

He snarled and leaped up at the great breakwater under the lowering sky. But it was too high.

The fishing boats sat safe as mice in their own mousehole. But they could not get out. And because the fishermen could not fish, there was no more food.

They ate up the few vegetables that were left in their storm-wracked gardens. They ate up the salted pilchards that were left in the cellars.

Mowzer hated vegetables and the pilchards were too salty for her taste.

Soon there was nothing left. The cats and their people grew very hungry.

Mowzer sat by her window, staring out at the storm, and thought longingly of morgy-broth and star-gazy pie.

Every day the fishermen gathered on the quayside and sometimes they would try to take a boat out through the Mousehole. But always the Great Storm-Cat lay in wait for them and they were lucky to escape with their lives.

ANTONIA BARBER

Slinky Malinki

Slinky Malinki
was blacker than black,
a stalking and lurking
adventurous cat.
He had bright yellow eyes,
a warbling wail
and a kink at the end
of his very long tail.

He was cheeky and cheerful,
friendly and fun,
he'd chase after leaves
and he'd roll in the sun.

But at night he was wicked
and fiendish and sly,
Through moonlight and shadow
he'd prowl and he'd pry.

He crept along fences,
he leaped over walls,
he poked into corners
and sneaked into halls.
What was he up to?
At night, to be brief,
Slinki Malinki
turned into a
THIEF.

All over town,
from basket and bowl,
he pilfered and pillaged,
he snitched and he stole.
Slippers and sausages,
biscuits, balloons,
brushes and bandages,
pencils and spoons.

He pulled them,
he dragged them,
he HEAVED them until …
he'd carried them home
to his house on the hill.

LYNLEY DODD

from The Story of the Cathedral and the Little Black Cat

'Good morning, Little Black Cat,' said the Cathedral.

'Miaow!' said the little black cat. 'Can I scratch my back against that little arch of yours ? I've got a tickle!'

'Of course,' said the Cathedral. 'Go ahead.'

The little black cat's name was Samuel, by the way. I think I'll call him Sam.

Sam rubbed his back. Oooooooooo! It was lovely.

He wandered inside and looked round. 'Miaow!' he said. 'You *are* big. A million cats could get in here.'

The Cathedral was very beautiful. There were a hundred tall candles inside, flickering brightly.

'Cathedral,' said Sam, 'what are cathedrals for?'

'Tell me first,' said the Cathedral, 'what are little black cats for?'

'For people to stroke,' said Sam, 'and to listen to us purring. Cats are very good for children. Especially babies. They like each other.'

'That is very good,' said the Cathedral. 'I am sure God cares for little black cats as well as for people.'

Sam was a bit puzzled. 'Who is God?' he said. 'Is he a "he" or a "she" or an "it"?'

'All of them,' said the Cathedral.

'Where does God live?' Sam asked.

'Here, there and everywhere.'

'In the sky?'

'There too!'

'Why doesn't he fall down?'

The Cathedral sighed and looked at the little black cat. 'God is inside your head.'

'Is he inside my tail, too?'

'If you think with your tail, he is,' said the Cathedral.

'Oh!'

'Now, I'll tell you what cathedrals are for. They are a special place for people to come and say their prayers.'

'Can cats say their prayers too?'

'Yes.'

'I will say my prayers now,' thought Sam.

DONALD BISSET

Badgers

Badgers come creeping from dark underground,
Badgers scratch hard with a bristly sound,
Badgers go nosing around.

Badgers have whiskers and black and white faces,
Badger cubs scramble and scrap and run races,
Badgers like overgrown places.

Badgers don't jump when a vixen screams,
Badgers drink quietly from moonshiny streams,
Badgers dig holes in our dreams.

Badgers are working while you and I sleep,
Pushing their tunnels down twisting and steep,
Badgers have secrets to keep.

RICHARD EDWARDS

from St Tiggywinkles Wildlife Hospital

He wasn't a very big badger and was hardly breathing as he
lay unconscious on the X-ray table. His short stubby legs were
splayed out on either side and there was a small trickle of
blood running down the white stripe of his black and white
marked face. He looked totally helpless.

'Ah, he does look sweet,' Sue said when she came into the
X-ray room.

I then had a brainwave. 'We'll call him Bisto, after the gravy
advertisement that says, 'Ah! Bisto.'

Our poor little badger was still unconscious, but at least he
now had a name.

I took the X-rays but couldn't find any trace of a bullet or
pellet, so I was fairly certain that Bisto had received his

injuries in a collision with a car. A small piece of broken bone
had come out through the skin causing the little hole that
looked like a bullet wound.

There was little more we could do at that time — it was by
now four o'clock in the morning — so I tucked him into a
warm cage and went back to bed.

By eight o'clock that morning, when I went to check him,
he hadn't moved at all. I was afraid he was going to die. But
as I looked closely at his injured head I could feel that he
was looking at me.

Then I saw one of his little black eyes water and blink as if
to say, 'Please help me.'

LES STOCKER

Badger

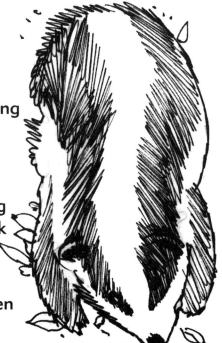

Through the trees I saw a badger
Early evening, nearly dusk
All the midges dancing round me
Foxglove scent, and ferny musk.

Through the trees I saw a badger
In the twilight, stars just out
Bats like rags were drifting, swooping
Sheep on hillside, farmer's shout

Through the trees I saw a badger
Through the air as grey as smoke
Light as dancers she came listening
Light as ghosts she sniffed the dark

Through the trees I saw a badger
Barred head lifted, wary, keen,
Then she faded through the bracken
Like a whisper, like a dream.

BERLIE DOHERTY

Sweet and Low

Sweet and low, sweet and low,
Wind of the western sea,
Low, low, breathe and blow,
Wind of the western sea!
Over the rolling waters go,
Come from the dying moon, and blow,
Blow him again to me;
While my little one, while my pretty one, sleeps.

Sleep and rest, sleep and rest,
Father will come to thee soon;
Rest, rest, on mother's breast,
Father will come to thee soon;
Father will come to his babe in the nest,
Silver sails all out of the west
Under the silver moon:
Sleep, my little one, sleep, my pretty one, sleep.

ALFRED, LORD TENNYSON

AESOP: Greek 6th century. *Aesop's Fables* is in Puffin 0140369848.

AGARD John: Guyanan born 1949. *The Speller's Bag* from *Grandfather's Old-Bruk-a-Down Car.* Bodley Head 1994. Red Fox 1997 ISBN 0099301407 © the author. Reprinted by permission Caroline Sheldon Agency.

AIKEN Joan: English born 1924. Extract from *The Last Slice of Rainbow* Puffin 0140323015 © the author.

ALLAN Nicholas: British. Extract from *Jesus' Christmas Party*. Hutchinson 1991. Red Fox 009972491X or mini-treasures edition 0099725916 © the author. Reprinted by permission of the publisher.

ALWAYS Jonathan: *The Sycamore Tree.*

ANDERSEN Hans: Danish 1805-1875. *The Princess and the Pea* from *Hans Andersen's Fairy Tales.* Retold and permission to reprint given by Naomi Lewis. Puffin Classics 0140367373.

ANONYMOUS: *New Shoes • The Sad Story of a Little Boy that Cried • Tonio's Gift,* taken from *The Friday Miracle,* edited by Kaye Webb. Puffin 1969. • *Hickory, Dickory, Dock • He was a rat, and she was a rat • How the Fir-Tree became our first Christmas Tree • The Gingerbread Boy.*

BANKS Lynne Reid: English born 1929. Extract from *The Indian in the Cupboard* published by Orion Children's Books 1981. Collins 0006730515 © the author.

BARBER Antonia: English 20th century. Extract from *The Mousehole Cat* © 1990 Antonia Barber, illustrated by Nicola Bayley. Reprinted by permission of the publisher Walker Books Ltd, London. 0744523532.

BARRETT David John: English 20th century. *An Injured Wasp.* Believed to be have been written while the writer was at Junior School.

BELL Anne: Australian 20th century. *The Donkey* from the anthology *Pardon My Garden* published Angus & Robertson/HarperCollins 0207172757 © the author.

BENNETT Rowena: English 20th century. *The Gingerbread Man* © the author.

BERG Leila: English 20th century. *Pete and the Ladybird* from *Little Pete Stories*. Methuen 1952. Also included in *The Oxford Treasury of Children's Stories*. Oxford University Press 019278112. © the author.

BISSETT Donald: English 20th century. Extract from *The Story of the Cathedral and the Little Black Cat* from *Please Yourself and Other Stories* by Donald Bissett. Methuen Children's Books/Reed International Books Ltd. © Reed Consumer Books 0749712430.

BLAKE William: English 1759-1827. *The Piper* from *Songs of Innocence; Tilly Lally* from *An Island in the Moon,* sung by Tilly Lally, a schoolboy. *Collected Poems* of William Blake.

BRIGGS Raymond: English born 1934. Extracts from *The Bear* Red Fox/Random House 0099385619. © the author. Reproduced by permission of the author and the publisher.

BROOKS Gwendolyn: African-American born 1917. *Keziah* from *Bronzeville Boys and Girls*. Harper & Row Inc. 1956. © the author and the publisher.

BROWN Ruth: English 20th century. Extract from *A Dark, Dark Tale*. Andersen Press 0862640016. Extract from *One Stormy Night* Andersen Press 0862644151. Reprinted by permission of the author/illustrator and the publisher.

BURNETT Frances Hodgson: English 1849-1924. Extract from *The Secret Garden* 1911. Puffin Classics 0140366660.

CAUSLEY Charles: English born 1917. *There was an Old Woman: I've Never Seen the Milkman* from *Early One Morning* and *Jack the Treacle Eater*, Macmillan Children's Books. Now included in *Collected Poems for Children* by Charles Causley, Macmillan 1996 0333625889. © the author and David Higham Associates.

CHAMBERS Nancy: American 20th century. *Florence Talltrees* from *Stir-A-Bout*. Julia MacRae Books, 1982. 0862030412 © the author.

CHAPMAN Jean: *Dressing Up* and *Puddle* from *Do You Remember What Happened?* Angus & Robertson, 1969.

CLARE John: English 1793-1864 *Little Trotty Wagtail* from any *Collected Poems* of John Clare.

CLARK Elizabeth: Extract from *Father Christmas and the Donkey* illustrated by Jan Ormerod. Puffin Books, 1993. 0140548890. © the author. Reproduced by permission of the author and Penguin Books Ltd.

COLLODI Carlo: Italian 1826-1890. Extract *from Pinocchio* first published 1882. Puffin Classics 014036708X.

Sources and Acknowledgements

CORNFORD Frances: English 1886-1960. *Night-Nursery Thoughts.*

CREBBIN June: English 20th century. *Cobweb Morning* from *The Jungle Sale.* Viking Kestrel 1988. Puffin 0140369597.

CROMPTON Richmal: English 1890-1969. Extract from *Aunt Arabelle in Charge* taken from *The Oxford Book of Children's Stories*, edited by Jan Mark 0192823973. Originally in *William – the Pirate*, Newnes 1932. © Macmillan Children's Books.

DAVEY Nicholas: Australian 20th century *Bad Luck, Dead Duck* from *Bad Luck, Dead Duck,* 1970. Dalton Publishers, Canberra, Australia 1971. ISBN 90990605X © the author.

DE LA MARE Walter: English 1873-1956. *The Fly; Some One* from *The Complete Poems of Walter de la Mare* 1969 Faber © The Literary Trustees of Walter de la Mare and the Society of Authors as their representative. Please note *Peacock Pie* Faber 0571149634 and *Collected Rhymes & Verses* Faber 0571111572 are still in print.

DODD Lynley: New Zealand born 1941. Extract from *Slinky Malinki* Puffin 0140544399 © the author/illustrator.

DODGE Mary Mapes: American 1831-1905. *That's What We'd Do.*

DOHERTY Berlie: English born 1943. *Badger* from *Walking on Air.* HarperCollins 0006744427. © the author. Reproduced by permission of the author and David Higham Associates.

DOUGLAS WIGGIN Kate: American 1856–1923. Extract from *Rebecca of Sunnybrook Farm* (1903) Puffin Classics 0140367594.

DOWLING Paul: English 20th century. Extract from *Hide and Shriek* A & C Black Publishers Ltd. Puffin 0140378324. Reproduced by permission of the author and publishers.

EDWARDS Richard: English born 1949. *Badgers; Susannah* from *The Word Party* by Richard Edwards. Lutterworth Press 1986. Puffin 0140320024. © the author. Reproduced by permission of the author and Felicity Bryan.

FARJEON Eleanor: English 1881-1965. *Keeping Christmas*; *To Any Garden.* Extract from *The Glass Skipper* (with Herbert Farjeon 1887-1945) now out of print but libraries might have the novel published Goodchild 1983. 0903445824. © Gervase Farjeon for the Estates of Eleanor and Herbert Farjeon.

FIELD Rachel: American 1894-1942. *The Dancing Bear* from *Taxis and Toadstools.* Doubleday and Company Inc. 1926.

FLEMING Elizabeth: English 20th century. *The Crumpled Rose-Leaf and the Real Princess* from *Gammon and Spinach.* Collins, 1927.

FLOURNEY Valerie: Extract from *The Patchwork Quilt* illustrated Jerry Pinkney. The Bodley Head 1985. Puffin 0140506411 © the author. Reproduced by permission of The Bodley Head.

FRENCH Vivian: English 20th century. Extract from *Caterpillar, Caterpillar* 1993 Vivian French, illustrated by Charlotte Voake. Reproduced by permission of Walker Books Ltd., London.

FYLEMAN Rose: English 1877-1957. *Regent's Park* from *Gay Go Up* Methuen 1929. Reproduced by permission of the Society of Authors as the Literary Representative of the Estate of Rose Fyleman.

GERAS Adèle: English born Jerusalem 1944. Extract from *A Lullaby for Freddie* from *Bedtime Stories for the Very Young* edited by Sally Grindley. Kingfisher 1856973395. © 1990 the author.

GODDEN Rumer: English born 1907. Extract from *The Story of Holly and Ivy.* Macmillan 1958. Puffin 0140305092. © the author. Reproduced by permission of the Curtis Brown Group Ltd.

GOWAR Mick: English born 1951. *Bridesmaid* from Let the Sun shine, edited by Kaye Webb. Francis Lincoln. 0711212473. © the author. Reproduced by permission of the author.

GRAHAME Kenneth: English 1859-1932. *Duck's Ditty* from *The Wind in the Willows* by Kenneth Grahame 1908. © The University Chest, Oxford. Reproduced by permission of the Curtis Brown Group Ltd, London.

GRAVES Robert: English 1895-1985. *Allie* from *Complete Poems of Robert Graves* Carcanet Press. Penguin Selected 014018483X. Reproduced by permission of the publishers on behalf of the estate of the late Robert Graves.

GREENAWAY Kate: English 1846-1901. *Three Little Girls* from *Under the Window,* 1878.

HADDON Mark: Extract from *The Sea of Tranquillity.* HarperCollins 1996. 0006645577. © the author. Reproduced by permission of the author and publisher.

HEATH-STUBBS John: English born 1918. *The Tawny Owl* from *A Parliament of Birds* Chatto & Windus 1975. *Collected Poems* Carcanet 1988. 0856357073. © the author.

HINDLEY Judy: English 20th century. Extract from *A Dragon's Bedtime* from *Bedtime Stories for the Very Young.* Kingfisher 1856973395. © the author.

HOBAN Russell: American, born 1925. *Tea Party; The Jigsaw Puzzle; Dragon Into Dressing Gown* from *The Pedalling Man* Mandarin/Reed International 1992 0749709138 and *The Last of the Wallendas* Hodder Children's Books, 1997. Extract from *The Mouse and His Child* Puffin Modern Classics 1969. 0140364552. © the author and David Higham Associates.

HOBERMAN Mary Ann: American born 1930. *Brother* from *Yellow Butter Purple Jelly Red Jam Black Bread.* © 1959/1987 the author.

HOUGH Charlotte: English born 1924. Extract from *The Tidying up of Thomas* taken from *Bad Boys* edited by Eileen Colwell. Puffin 0140305300. © the author.

HUDDY Delia: English born 1934. Extract from *The Nearly Ghost Baby* A & C Black (Publishers) Ltd. Puffin 0140381236. © the author.

HUGHES Shirley: English born 1929. Extract from *Alfie's Feet.* Red Fox/Random House Children's Books 0099256061. © the author. Reproduced by permission of author and publisher.

IPCAR Dahlov: *Fishes Evening Song* from *Whisperings and Other Things* Alfred A Knopf 1967. © the author.

JACKSON Leroy: American. *Grandpa Dropped His Glasses* from *Child Life* Magazine. © Rand-McNally Co.

JAMES Richard: *The Barn Owl.*

JONES Terry: English 20th century. Extracts from *The Wonderful Cake-Horse* and *The Three Raindrops* taken from *Terry Jones Fairy Tales.* illustrated by Michael Foreman, Pavilion Books 1981. Puffin 1983. 0140316426. © the author. Reproduced by permission of Pavilion Books.

KEATS John: English 1795-1821. Extract from *A Song of Myself,* from *Collected Poems* of Keats.

KENWARD Jean: English born 1920. *Icicle Joe* from *Seasons* Blackie 0216927560 © 1989 the author.

KING Paul: Extract from *Teddy Bear's Picnic.* Reproduced by permission of the author and Samuel French Ltd. 0573122679

LEE Dennis: Canadian born 1939. *The Muddy Puddle* from *Garbage Delight* Macmillan of Canada 1977 0771595921 © 1977 Dennis Lee. Reproduced with the author's permission.

LEWIS Naomi: English 20th century. *The Princess and the Pea* as translator - see Andersen.

MARK Jan: English born 1943. Extract from *The Short Voyage of the Albert Ross* Puffin 0140369139. Reproduced by permission of the author.

McGOUGH Roger: English, born 1937. *Bully Night* from *Sky in the Pie* Kestrel 1983. Puffin 0140316124. © the author. Reproduced by permission of the Peters Fraser and Dunlop Group.

McKEE David: English 20th century. *King Rollo and the Tree.* Reproduced by permission of the author/illustrator, David McKee and Andersen Press, London 0862648703.

MILNE A. A.: English 1882-1956. *Knight-in-Armour; Swing Song* from *Now We Are Six* Methuen Children's Books/ Reed International Books Ltd 0749702087. Reproduced by permission of Reed Consumer Books Ltd.

MITCHISON Naomi: English born 1898. Extract from *Nix Nought Nothing.* Although the play is out of print the story may be found in *English Fairy Tales* by Joseph Jacobs. Puffin Classics 0140367853.

NICHOLS Grace: Guyanan born 1950. *Give Yourself a Hug; Making My First Snowman in My Mother's Pink Rubber Gloves* from *Give Yourself a Hug* A & C Black, 1994. Puffin 0140372180. Reproduced by permission of Curtis Brown Ltd London, on behalf of Grace Nichols. © Grace Nichols, 1994.

PEARCE Philippa: English, born 1920. Extract from *A Dog So Small* 1962. Puffin Modern Classics 0140372342 or Puffin Fiction 0140302069. © the author and reproduced with her permission.

PRELUTSKY Jack: American, born 1940. *I am a Ghost Who's Lost His Boo* from *Something Big Has Been Here* Heinemann/Reed International Books Ltd. Mammoth 0749710144 © the author with the permission of the publisher.

Sources and Acknowledgements

REEVES James: English 1909–1978. *Mrs Button; The Intruder; The Wind* from *Complete Poems for Children* Mammoth 0749735023. © James Reeves. Reprinted by permission of the James Reeves Estate.

RICE Tim and LLOYD WEBBER Andrew: English 20th century. Extract from *Joseph and His Amazing Technicolor Dreamcoat* © The Really Useful Group Ltd, London 1969. Vocal Score published by the Really Useful Group Ltd. Cat no: RUG 37234. Our text from Puffin 014050432X.

ROBERTS Elizabeth Madox: American 1886-1941. *Cinderella's Song.*

ROBINSON Joan G: English 20th century. Extract from *Teddy Robinson Goes Up A Tree* from *Dear Teddy Robinson* Puffin 1966 0140307362. © Joan G. Robinson 1956/1960. Reproduced by permission of Penguin Books Ltd.

ROSSETTI Christina: Italian-English 1830-1894. *Caterpillar; The Wind* in *Sing-Song* Dover Books 0486221075.

SCHENK DE REGNIERS Beatrice: American born 1914. Extract from *A Little House of Your Own* Collins 1957, now out of print.

SHARP William (pseudonym: Fiona McLeod): Scottish 1855-1905. *The Wasp.*

SILVERSTEIN Shel: American, born 1932. *Rain* from *Where the Sidewalk Ends* Harper & Row (Publishers) Inc. 1974. © the author.

SIMPSON Matt: English, born 1936. *One Spring Day* from *The Pig's Thermal Underwear* by Matt Simpson Headland 090307477X and *Matt, Wes and Pete: Sandwich Poets* Macmillan 0330338757. © the author.

STEPHENS James: Irish 1882-1950. *The White Window* from *Collected Poems* Macmillan 1926. Permission to reproduce given by the Society of Authors as the Literary Representative of the Estate of James Stephens.

STEVENSON Robert Louis: Scottish 1850–1894. *A Good Play; Looking-Glass River* from *A Child's Garden of Verses*. Various editions.

STOCKER Les: English 20th century. Extract from *St Tiggywinkles Wildlife Hospital* HarperCollins 1995. 0006751814. © the author. Permission to reproduce given by the publisher.

STREATFEILD Noel: English 1895-1986. Extract from *Curtain Up* Dent, 1944. Taken from Puffin edition 014031511X. Permission to reproduce given by the publisher on behalf of the Literary Estate of the author.

TENNYSON Alfred, Lord: English 1809-1892. *Sweet and Low* from any *Collected Poems* of Tennyson.

TODD Barbara Euphan: English 1890-1976. Extract from *Worzel Gummidge* © 1936 the author. Permission to reproduce given by the Estate of the late Barbara Euphan Todd and A. M. Heath and Co. Ltd.

TURNBULL Ann: English 20th century. Extract from *The King of the Blue Lagoon.* © Ann Turnbull 1991. From *Bedtime Stories for the Very Young* compiled by Sally Grindley. Kingfisher 1856973395, by permission of David Higham Associates.

WADDELL Martin: Irish born 1941. Extract from *Owl Babies* © 1992 Martin Waddell illustrated by Patrick Benson, Walker Books 0744531675. Extract from *The Toymaker* © 1991 Martin Waddell illustrated by Terry Milne, Walker Books 0744530180. Both extracts reproduced by permission of the publisher.

WALSH John: English 1911–1972. *Taking Out Jim* from *Poets in Hand* edited Anne Harvey Puffin 1984. © Patrick Walsh on behalf of the Estate of John Walsh.

Anne Harvey trained at the Guildhall School of Music & Drama and on leaving founded the Guildhall Players Repertory Company in Perranporth, Cornwall. She has taught drama, examined for the Guildhall School, Poetry Society and London University, and now works freelance in broadcasting, writing and presenting literary programmes. She has edited over thirty anthologies of poetry and drama, winning the Signal award in 1992.

> 'Our most eclectic and engaged anthologiser for children.'
>
> *Times Educational Supplement.*

The Guildhall School of Music & Drama is a world-class drama and music conservatoire and the leader in graded examinations, setting standards for music, drama and speech communication around the world. Creative skills together with confident speaking and listening have never been more important than in our time. The Guildhall's graded syllabuses are based on more than a century of tradition combined with a modern and innovative educational philosophy. They help to develop key transferable skills for life, such as personal expression, sensitivity to others, cultural awareness and identity. Above all, they help to develop intuitive, aesthetic and imaginative thinking, focusing on the intrinsic value of engaging in artistic forms of experience.

The Corporation of London is the local authority for the financial and commercial heart of Britain, the City of London. As sponsor of the arts the Corporation ranks among the most generous in the country, following only the Government and the BBC. The Guildhall School of Music & Drama, owned and funded by the Corporation of London and renowned as a centre of excellence, is part of the Corporation's ongoing commitment to the development of the arts and the international cultural scene in the Square Mile.

CORPORATION
OF LONDON

Notes